For Jack —

who will recognize
many "old friends" —
with regards from the
editors.

John & James

BOOKBINDING
IN AMERICA
1680–1910

From the Collection of
Frederick E. Maser

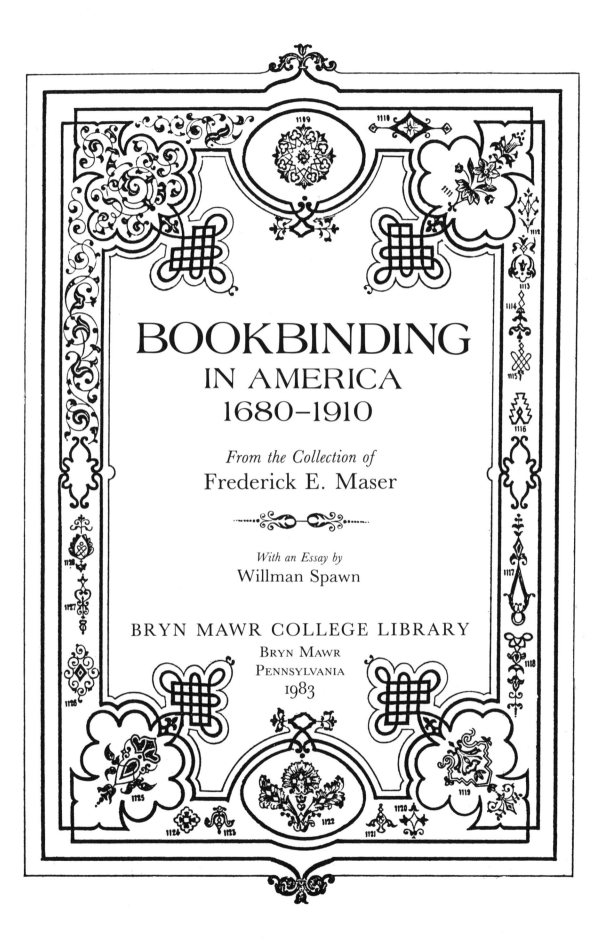

BOOKBINDING
IN AMERICA
1680–1910

From the Collection of
Frederick E. Maser

With an Essay by
Willman Spawn

BRYN MAWR COLLEGE LIBRARY
BRYN MAWR
PENNSYLVANIA
1983

The publication of this volume has been supported in part by FREDERICK E. and MARY LOUISE JARDEN MASER and DANIEL and JOANNA SEMEL ROSE.

The frontispiece is entry no. 17: "A Philadelphia Binding by Robert Aitken's Shop, 1799." The cover vignette is from Edward Hazen, *The Panorama of Professions and Trades,* Philadelphia, 1836 (Gift of Dr and Mrs Klaus Hummeler). The vignette used on pages 37 and 117 is from John Adems Paxton, *The Philadelphia Directory and Registry for 1819,* Philadelphia, [1818] (The Adelman Collection). The border of the title page is from Gaskill & Copper, *Patterns . . . for Ornamenting the Covers of Books,* Philadelphia, 1847.

Copyright © 1983 Bryn Mawr College Library

Library of Congress Catalog Card Number 83-72595

Distributed by the University Press of Virginia, Charlottesville, Virginia 22903

Dedicated to
MARY LOUISE JARDEN MASER
in whose honor the collection has been given
to Bryn Mawr College Library

Table of Contents

The Occasion

THE OCCASION OF THIS STUDY is the gift to the Bryn Mawr College Library of the Frederick E. Maser Collection of American bookbindings. Their place in the Library's collections and their significance for the study of this art will be the subject of the pages which follow. Our indebtedness to Dr and Mrs Maser extends well beyond the books themselves. Most important is their concern that their treasures be placed where students and other scholars can readily profit by their availability.

JAMES TANIS
DIRECTOR OF LIBRARIES

Introduction by the Donor

The Human Element of a Bookbinding Collection

A YOUNG MAN WAS VISITING a book-collector friend. While waiting in the library for his host, he drew a drab looking book from the shelf. It was a fragile but perfect copy of the first edition of Keats' *Endymion* in the original paper boards. Suddenly it slipped from his hands, hitting the floor at an angle knocking off the front cover and damaging the title page. Just then his host entered.

"I'm afraid I've ruined one of your books. I surely hope it wasn't valuable."

"Tut tut," said the book collector trying desperately to be the perfect host. "It was nothing—absolutely noth. . . ." And then he fainted dead away!

Any knowledgeable collector might well have fainted. But many people would have difficulty in understanding why anyone would feel and act this way about an old book and its homely binding.

Why does a person spend years and years rooting in basements, climbing ladders in book shops at some personal risk, writing to dealers halfway around the world and visiting public auctions to salvage a few hundred books?

There are many reasons—enough, at least, to make me cautious about lending any of my books. Still the question remains, why collect books and particularly bookbindings?

For me, a sound reason for collecting books is that a wisely chosen collection can open to one's imagination an unexplored world of literary thought and practice. A collection can reflect a period in history. It can reveal a step or series of steps in the development of humankind. It can show us in part how we came to be. This is the human element in the collecting of books and, in this case, bookbindings.

When I mention bookbindings, I am not referring to the personal inscriptions that often appear on the inside of the book covers. I have in my library books with handwritten notes that could be the basis for a dramatic story or a dark tragedy, or that refer to rollicking good times. However, this is a subject all its own, on which someone else might well write an essay. I am referring rather to those human attitudes, ideas and social practices that can be discovered through a close study of American bookbindings. If art is a universal language, then the art of bookbinding should speak to us forcefully.

Avenues of Approach

A study of early American bookbindings reveals, for one thing, which nations exerted the greatest influence on the Colonies. Binders, in the beginning, brought with them and followed the ideas of the shops in the British Isles and Continental Europe. There is little about the early bindings to suggest the direct influence of Southern Europe, China or the Middle East. As these influences developed in our country they were partially reflected in our furniture, wallpaper design and chinaware; but only at a later period in bookbindings. The early bookbinders followed a more traditional trend. While seeking the fashionable, they were not faddists.

Another approach to the subject is to note some books our ancestors thought worth preserving. It is true that many of the products of the early American presses were more or less ephemeral—newspapers, almanacs, broadsides, etc. Magazines, however, were sometimes issued as annuals in permanent bindings. Other productions also preserved in leather included the journals and laws of the colonial assemblies. Americans apparently valued law and order. They may have been revolutionaries; they were not anarchists. It naturally followed that books about the law also became important. *Every Man His Own Lawyer* (entry no. 12) soon became popular. The need for medical care in the Colonies led to *Every Man His Own Doctor*, causing the irrepressible Benjamin Franklin to remark there probably soon would be a book on *Every Man His Own Priest*. Certainly a careful study of the early titles that were issued and sometimes reissued and preserved in solid bindings will reveal much about the lives and customs of our forefathers.

In New England and in the Middle Atlantic States theological books, sermons, devotional literature and Bibles, and in the South particularly, the classics and poetry were important to our ancestors. We most surely learn something about a country that preserved in sturdy covers *The Imitation of Christ*—a book published not by one house but by a number of printing establishments—and which, by 1815, was being printed as far west as Ohio. By 1812 printers in at least nine of the thirteen original Colonies had published Bibles or parts of the Bible in strong, permanent bindings. This fact is astounding, especially when one considers the logistic difficulties in the vast expenditure of funds necessary for printing a book of such size. Yet, so popular were well-bound Bibles that Matthew Carey of Philadelphia (1760–1839) kept one, possibly two in standing type. By 1800 a Greek New Testament had been published in America followed by numerous other editions. Some of these books were in simple calf bindings, others in gift bindings, reflecting the importance of religion in the New World.

Bindings even reveal the religious attitudes and the general religious concepts of the people who owned them. Note the strongly bound Bibles of Christopher Sauer and many of the other books of the Pennsylvania Germans. Notice on some the strength-giving guards, the brass corners, and the leather and metal clasps. These are bindings made to hold a book of permanent worth. They point to a strong belief in the God who rules the world with dignity, wisdom and power.

The more graceful bindings on religious books—those of an Aitken, Buglass or Legge—suggest that Americans had also discovered beauty in creation and in the world where they lived. God was to be seen and revealed not only in the sermon of the preacher but also in the handicraft of the artist. There was nothing incongruous in placing a beautiful binding on a Bible or prayer book. It was a worthy tribute to books necessary for the full appreciation of life. It reflects an attitude in keeping with the religious movements that on various occasions shook the Colonies and the young Republic.

Bindings also reveal cultural patterns. Gift bindings were often placed on books to be handed down from generation to generation. The American settlers, in general, appreciated books, preserved them, gave them to succeeding generations—even through their wills—and thus demonstrated that American culture was permanently committed to the importance of reading and education. Little wonder that schools, colleges and universities were soon established in the New World and that eventually an education became the right of every person.

THE BRYN MAWR CONNECTION

From the moment the Director of Libraries, James Tanis, and his associate, Mary S. Leahy, first saw my collection they expressed an appreciation and enthusiasm that warmed my heart. That is one reason why I am happy that the collection has been placed at Bryn Mawr. A survey of this book and the exhibition will reveal his tenacious research and that of his associate John Dooley. They have been indefatigable in attempting to track down the history of the binders and their shops, their special skills and their methods of production. They have even secured on loan from the James Macdonald Company, some of the tools of this ancient craft.

In addition, I wish to thank James Tanis personally for his gift to Bryn Mawr of a John Ratcliff binding which fills an important gap in my collection.

Mary Leahy and her staff have handled the books with skill and care. Through the use of modern conservation techniques they have restored each volume to its finest condition. What collector could be other than happy with the results, as well as with the tasteful and intelligent display arranged with her help and direction.

Willman Spawn, a leading authority on early American bindings, has contributed an informative essay to introduce this collection to the public. I wish to thank him for

this contribution which only he could make and also for his gift to Bryn Mawr of an important double-panel Boston binding.

I am also grateful that through my contact with Bryn Mawr I have become more closely associated with some of my fellow book collectors, particularly Seymour Adelman, whose own gifts to Bryn Mawr have brought additional prestige to a great institution. His splendid ticketed binding by Samuel Taylor of Philadelphia is an important document in the history of Pennsylvania binding.

Finally, it is obvious that the scholarly program of this distinguished library has been assured by the encouragement of an appreciative President, Faculty, Board of Trustees and Friends of the Library.

FREDERICK E. MASER

14

Preface by the Editors

THE FULL STORY OF BOOKBINDING in America is a tale yet to be told. A flurry of interest by the Grolier Club members at the turn of the century gave form to the field. Since that time, however, except for occasional episodic interest, extensive and intensive research has largely been in the hands of Hannah D. French and Willman Spawn. Dorothy Miner's epic-making exhibition—"The History of Bookbinding, 525–1950 A.D."—held at the Baltimore Museum of Art in 1957–58 placed a few major American bindings in the context of a comprehensive international survey, but the most extensive picture to date was provided by the 1972 catalog of selections from the Michael Papantonio Collection prepared by Miss French and Mr Spawn.

Before the arrival of the Maser Collection, Bryn Mawr's most significant American bindings had come to the Library as a result of that bibliopegistic interest evinced by the Grolier Club and its offspring, the Club Bindery. The first and foremost group of books came to Bryn Mawr from Helen Annan Scribner, Bryn Mawr Class of 1891 and wife of Arthur Hawley Scribner, a Grolier member and a stockholder in the Club Bindery. This study includes works given by Mrs Scribner and executed by New York's two leading binders of the day, Henry Stikeman (no. 58) and James Macdonald (no. 62). A choice example of the work of the Club Bindery (no. 61) was the gift of Mrs Scribner's friend Alba Boardman Johnson, Bryn Mawr Class of 1889.

In the years of the last decade of the nineteenth century a growing interest in hand binding accompanied the revival of hand printing, particularly in the dramatic publications of William Morris. The leading spirit was one of England's greatest binders and William Morris' friend T. J. Cobden-Sanderson. Morris' Kelmscott Press was paralleled by Cobden-Sanderson's Doves Bindery. (Incidentally, the first book bound at the Doves Bindery was given to Bryn Mawr by Mrs Scribner.) In England this movement inspired the creation of the Guild of Women Binders. Their enthusiasm crossed the Atlantic and several fine female hand binders appeared in the States. An account of this movement is still to be written but we have included one early work by Bryn Mawrtyr Frances Arnold of the Class of 1897. (no. 60)

Though the Scribner bindings were among the finest examples produced, their full usefulness for the student of bookbinding awaited the coming of Dr Maser's four-hundred volumes. Now the few extraordinary bindings already here take on new significance and usefulness. Certainly no more elegant perspective could be provided than that given by the two volumes of the Aitkens' majestic red morocco "Hot Press" Bible.

In choosing the sixty-two entries for this study, we strove to complement the Papantonio catalog. Though we began at the same place—with America's first identified binder, John Ratcliff—we have extended the coverage to the first years of the present century and the conscious reestablishment of the hand-binding tradition. We have omitted Maser bindings which can be studied in Papantonio's examples, the anonymous Philadelphia binding on Godman's *American Natural History* and S. Moore's binding on *The Gift . . . for 1842*. Instead, you will find several pairs of bindings which demonstrate varied handlings of similar books. We have also included a small group of previously unpublished Exeter, New Hampshire, bindings and a broader sampling of Pennsylvania German work.

All of the bindings are illustrated and placed as near their entries as possible. The notable exception is the location of the color illustrations, which are grouped following page 17. Citations are in chronological order with the exception of the Aitkens' Bible and certain entries with two bindings. These compare examples of work by one binder or are related in some other way. To the extent identified, each entry details the place where a book was bound, the name of the binder or shop, and the approximate date of binding. Measurements are given in centimeters to the nearest tenth with height given first, width second and thickness third.

The physical description of a binding begins with mention of the type of leather. The color of leather is stated only if it is other than that of a tanned skin. Additional elements described are: the decoration of the boards, the spine, the board edges, the turn-ins, the endpapers and page edges. It is to be understood that binders' board was used for a book's covers unless wooden board is specifically stated.

For provenance we have cited all previous ownership noted in the books and have transcribed and quoted the details as found. We have attempted to list the provenance of each work in chronological order. In the references, notice has been made to specific studies with relevant information. General information can be found most readily in the volumes cited in the selected bibliography on p. 115. Evans, Shaw and Shoemaker have been cited for the appropriate American imprints. Reference has been made to Papantonio in cases where there are points of comparison with entries in this study.

As in most scholarly undertakings, we have been mightily helped along the way by the aid and encouragement of others. Any measure of usefulness this volume may have must be credited to Willman Spawn, whose involvement began with advice on the selection of the books to be included and continues with his enlightening paper. The interested and informed involvement of Carol Spawn has also greatly strengthened this project. Hannah French too has been of invaluable assistance, generously sharing the results of her many years of research.

Those persons to whom we are further indebted include: Barbara C. M. Dudley of Albany, New York; Nancy Burkett of the American Antiquarian Society; Cesi Kellinger and George Hall Jr of Chambersburg, Pennsylvania; Richard J. Wolfe of the Francis A. Countway Library of Medicine; Jacques Desmonts of the James Macdonald Co. of East Norwalk, Connecticut; Herbert B. Anstaett of the Evangelical and Reformed Historical Society; Charles Gilman Hayes and Nancy C. Merrill of Exeter, New Hampshire; Kathleen Moretto and Robert Siever of Franklin and Marshall College Library; Robert Nikirk of the Grolier Club; Edwin Wolf 2nd of the Library Company of Philadelphia; Robert Ewald and Peter van Wingen of the Library of Congress; Katherine M. Richards of the New-York Historical Society; Vernon Gunnion and Nadine Steinmetz of the Pennsylvania Farm Museum of Landis Valley; Sandy Stelts of the Pennsylvania State University Library; Thomas Knoles of Rutgers University Library; and Mrs Ronald Macdonald of Rye, New Hampshire.

16

At Bryn Mawr College Library we owe special thanks to Karl Dimler and his student assistant, Geneva Brinton, for the fine photographs of the bindings and other materials reproduced in this volume; to Mary S. Leahy who has arranged the exhibition and has been critically involved in every stage of this book; to M. Winslow Lundy who has provided editorial assistance in addition to a variety of other tasks; to our secretaries Mary Devlin, Virginia Harpold and Rita Sohmer; and to our students, Shizhe Huang, Chiyo Ishikawa, Megan Gerard Klose, Susan Goodrich Lehmann and Marguerite Anne Robbins, who undertook chores ranging from preserving the bindings to providing the initial research for the entries. Many other staff members have been helpfully involved in the numerous tasks generated by this project. It is our hope that the usefulness of this volume will be commensurate to the effort and dedication which has made it a reality.

JOHN DOOLEY
JAMES TANIS

PLATE I   *A New York Binding Attributed to Henry I. Megarey, ca. 1819 (entry no. 30).*

19

PLATE II *A Chambersburg, Pennsylvania, Binding for the Publication Office of the German Reformed Church, ca. 1842 (entry no. 44).*

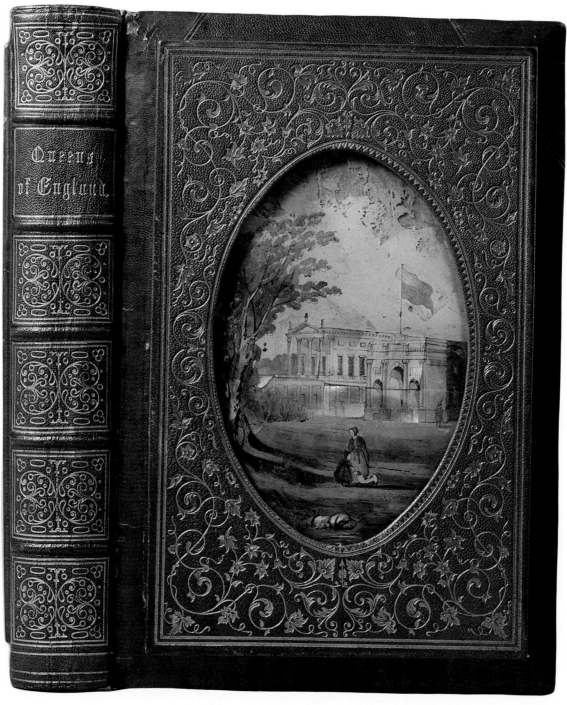

PLATE III   *A New York Binding for D. Appleton & Company, ca. 1851 (entry no. 50).*

PLATE IV   *A New York Binding for Riker, Thorne & Co., ca. 1854 (entry no. 51).*

25

PLATE V   *A Philadelphia Binding by Pawson & Nicholson, ca. 1855 (entry no. 52).*

27

The Evolution of American Binding Styles
in the Eighteenth Century

BY WILLMAN SPAWN

AMERICAN BOOKBINDING had its known beginning in Boston about 1662, when John Ratcliff was engaged to come from England to bind the newly published Eliot Indian Bible. Although other early binders, known by their names only, lived in Boston, New Jersey and Maryland, Ratcliff was the first whose documented work has survived for us to see. (no. 1) This is typical of the history of bookbinders in general. With the exception of major figures, it consists only of lists of names of craftsmen and their localities, and of descriptions of styles. Most binders in any period are anonymous workers, unlike their colleagues the printers, whose names appear on almost every piece of their work. Apart from the occasional documented binding, the binders of the great majority of leather-bound books may be identified only by their style of decoration. It has been my attempt for the last thirty years to do just that for eighteenth-century American bookbinding: to link the books and their makers through the tools that they used. On this research I have based this paper on the evolution of American binding styles.

When the eighteenth century began, there were two main centers of the book trade in the Colonies. Boston was in the lead followed by Philadelphia; New York was some distance behind. In each city, printing consisted primarily of official government records, religious works of many types, almanacs, manuals and "how to" books, and pamphlets. Not all of this production was put into leather covers, but rather was issued in paper covers. Because of their fragility and their frequently ephemeral character, these probably did not survive very long. Of the leather-bound books that have come down to us from the early 1700s, most are in very plain bindings of sheepskin, tooled on the boards in a panel design, but with the spines left bare. (no. 2) This simplicity is not a testimony to lack of skill on the part of the binder, but rather to the popularity of that style. When a more elaborate decoration was called for, on a compilation of laws or a presentation copy, for example, the same binders were equal to the task.

The craftsmen who produced America's colonial bindings were trained and organized in the customary apprentice/journeyman/master pattern. The standard shop consisted of a master and his family, with a live-in, unpaid apprentice or two, bound out to learn the trade for seven years or until he was twenty-one. I know of no women binders in the first half of the century, although it seems likely that the women in the household took their turns at the sewing frames. In good times, when business flourished, or in a large shop, one or more journeymen binders would be employed for wages. These were men trained as binders who lacked the capital or education or perhaps the desire to be masters in their own shops. The term *journeyman*, meaning a man hired to do work by the day, also fits another aspect of these men's lives, for they formed the mobile portion of the binding trade, moving from shop to shop, from town to town, as opportunity or the lack of it dictated.

Before detailing the evolution of binding styles, I will describe my method for identifying binders by the tools they used. For more than three decades I have systematically collected rubbings of decorated leather bindings on three categories of books: eighteenth-century American imprints, that is, books printed in America between 1700 and 1800; European imprints in bindings proven American by internal evidence or documentation; and non-printed items with American provenance, say the manuscript journal of a Philadelphia Quaker or the account books of a Boston business. It has been my belief that if I gathered sufficient evidence in the form of such rubbings eventually I could link all the various appearances of a particular tool; distinguish it from any other tool of similar design; establish the time span over which it was used; and, finally, assign it to the shop of a particular bookbinder through supporting documentation. I have in fact been able to do this for at least 137 bookbinders to date.

The decorations I rely on were created by the use of hand-engraved tools, stamps and rolls, heated and applied to the dampened leather, where they leave their impressions in reverse. Hand stamps are single designs engraved on the face of a brass shank and attached to a handle; they are used at the corners of panels, in the center of a board, in the compartments of a spine. Rolls are repetitive designs engraved on the circumference of a brass wheel, mounted in a handle, so that the wheel produces a continuous pattern as it is revolved, under considerable pressure from the binder. (The decorative roll was used in Germany at least as early as the 1460s, and was in common use in Europe by 1520.) Straight lines called *fillets* are the most common rolls; undulating ribbons, stylized flowers and vines, and Greek keys are among the many other designs that come to mind.

Although a few gold-tooled bindings appeared in seventeenth-century Boston and elsewhere in America until the mid-eighteenth century, tooled decoration was almost always produced in blind. Even the plainest bindings, tooled only with fillets, might carry a decorative roll on the board edges. This is so inconspicuous as sometimes to be more visible on the rubbing than to the naked eye. It has proven invaluable in the process of linking plain bindings to those with more extensive decoration.

Very little is known about the source of the binders' tools used in eighteenth-century America. The earliest known advertisement of an American engraver of tools appeared in a Boston paper in 1745. The first tools must have come with their users across the Atlantic; after that, presumably, they were imported from suppliers-to-the-trade in London and other cities. It is noticeable that new designs that appeared on books bound in London, Edinburgh and Dublin, within a few years were appearing on books bound in America. The strong supposition is that the tools to produce the fashionable designs were imported from engravers in those cities. Importation of tools continued even after the Revolution. There is documentation for this in Robert Aitken's accounts: the purchase of a decorative roll from Timbury of London in 1790. This is an aspect of American binding history that has received little attention.

The attempt to single out the various appearances of a particular decorative roll or stamp calls for close examination of all rubbings showing that design. In the case of a hand stamp, there are the obvious differences which distinguish one tool from another of the same design: a nick or slip in the engraving, a worn spot, a design element that is different between the two. One of my favorite stamps is the late eighteenth-century design I call the "Bird in the Bush," cut in two versions. In one the tail goes up, in the other the tail goes down. Would that all tools were as easy to distinguish from each other as these!

The comparison becomes more tricky in the case of decorative rolls. Once the visible differences have been eliminated, there may still be left two rolls of striking similarity. In this case it is imperative to check the exact length of each unit on one roll, hoping thereby to pick up an irregularity that will distinguish it from its partner. This is done with an ingenious instrument called a ten-unit divider. Because the tools are cut by hand and because it is difficult to construct the repeats so that the first and last unit join perfectly, there are always small adjustments and compensations that occur. If a comparison of the divider patterns of the two rolls reveals that there is indeed an irregularity present in one and not the other, then they must be two different rolls. The divider pattern can be recorded and used to distinguish these rolls from each other, wherever they appear. I now estimate that one out of every four or five rolls is similar enough to another to require the use of the divider technique.

Unless I have really substantial documentation for a tool—a binder's label or an inscription in the book, a binder's bill or an invoice from a printer or a library mentioning the exact title—I have made it a rule to assign a new tool to a specific binder *only* when I find it used in combination with two or more tools known as his. This may seem overcautious, and it has indeed led to a sort of limbo for tools that I cannot link to a particular stock. However, the decoration of bindings followed the fashion, just as clothing, furniture and amusements did. Therefore, books published at the same time are likely to be decorated in the same style, with tools that may not be identical but give the same appearance. Each binder of enough skill and stature to follow the fashion would attempt to use the same tool design, hence the need for such close comparison.

There are a few other traps for the unwary which I will mention. The binding on a dated book cannot predate that book, but it can postdate it by any amount of time. That is, a book printed in 1753 could not have been bound in 1750, but it could have been bound in 1754, 1760, 1770, or indeed any year one chooses. The appearance of a binding can be altered, and this has often been done by adding gold tooling, title labels and ornament where it did not exist on the original. And finally, when comparing the ways in which tools appear, it is wise to compare their use on the same type of book, that is, a folio law book with a folio law book rather than a presentation prayer book. There were certain conventions followed for designs in both these cases, which influenced the kinds of tools that were used.

Now let us proceed to the evolution of styles. In Boston, at the beginning of the eighteenth century, the predominating style on all sizes and types of bindings was the double panel on the board, created by the use of single-line fillets in combination with a decorative roll, set off by a hand stamp placed diagonally outside the four corners. (no. 8) The spine was plain, without any decoration or title lettering. The endpapers were plain. Often the decorative roll from the board, or a different roll, was used on the board edges, as described before. The tooling generally was in blind. The leather for this style of binding, as for almost every other binding produced in the eighteenth century to the time of the Revolution, was sheep, a coarser and less elegant material than calf. Sheep was undoubtedly cheaper, whether local or imported, and reasonably durable. At least in the early part of the century, when calf was used, it was imported as was morocco. Morocco, called *turkey* in binders' parlance, was used once in a great while on very special bindings such as presentation prayer books.

Other styles were also in use. The single panel, with a hand stamp at the corners, decorated some books, usually smaller ones. (no. 2) On a few books the binder omitted any panel and simply outlined the four sides of the cover with a single- or double-line fillet; this seems to have been a style for inexpensive books. In the 1730s and 1740s an innovation appears in the form of a decorative roll run down along the spine and close to it, inside the spine fillet. (no. 7) It is the same time that gold tooling makes its reappearance in Boston. According to Hannah D. French, whose study of Boston bindings has been extensive, the earliest known eighteenth-century gold-tooled Boston binding was produced in 1737, on a red morocco prayer book that combines the single-panel side with a decorated spine. From this time on the gold-tooled decorated spine will appear on Boston books with some frequency, but the paneled sides, the decorative border and the spine roll will continue as the basic binding styles until mid-century.

As in any research, there are always a few pieces of information that do not fit into the constructed thesis. There are two such pieces for Boston in this period. First, I have records of four bindings that combine blind-paneled boards with gold-tooled spines and filleted borders on the edges. They look almost as if the binder could not decide which style to follow and so used them all. However, they are not the work of one binder. I consider them a transitional form from one style to another. The second awkward piece of information is the use of the title labels on a number of copies of the folio edition of Samuel Willard's *A Compleat Body of Divinity* published in Boston in 1726. These title labels are ten years earlier than any others I have recorded. There is no evidence that they were added later or were not part of the original binding. Indeed, their close similarity makes the latter origin seem more likely. Why then did the innovation fail to catch on in 1726, yet become almost instant with most Boston binders in the 1740s?

As we turn to Philadelphia, it is of interest to note that my Philadelphia records for the early part of the century are only a third the size of my Boston records for that period. The striking difference between the cities is confirmed by a bookseller's observation, that there are many more books available in New England than in the Middle Atlantic States. The explanation may lie in this. Printing in Boston began in 1639 and continued strong. Printing in Philadelphia began in 1685 with William Bradford, who left for New York in 1693, having incurred the disfavor of the Quaker hierarchy. The craft limped along, producing little of any size until the publication of the Laws of Pennsylvania in 1714. Early Boston printing is full of catechisms, psalm books, church platforms and covenants, and sermons, all the apparatus of established religion. It seems clear that the Massachusetts theocracy depended on the printed word to inform, educate and ultimately control its adherents. In contrast, the Quaker theocracy was *anti*-establishment, depending on religious enthusiasm and oral witnessing. The tight control by the committee of overseers of the press, the only press in the colony, must have discouraged publishing. Until the addition of a second press in 1723, there cannot have been any "freedom of the press" as we understand the term. Finally, Harvard College was founded in 1636, and its first published thesis is recorded in 1642. Each succeeding year Evans' *American Bibliography* includes one or more entries from the college. Philadelphia had no comparable institution until well into the eighteenth century.

Despite the disparity in the quantity of printing and hence of binding done in the two cities, the records do reveal the same styles predominating in Philadelphia in the first decades of the eighteenth century. We find the tooling in blind, the double panel, the plain spine, the single panel on smaller books after its initial appearance in 1728, the decorative roll around the edges of the boards, finally the use of a roll paralleling the spine. All these we have seen in Boston in approximately the same sequence. Even gold tooling was introduced in Philadelphia in the same decade as in Boston, appearing in 1733 on a morocco psalm book, ornately decorated but with an untitled spine. In Philadelphia the first decorated spine with a tooled title appears in 1744, coincident with the arrival of Joseph Goodwin from England, who advertises that he can bind "in the neatest Manner now practis'd, gilt and letter'd, or plain."

I have spoken so far only of bindings on printed books, for I admit that my records of blankbooks and non-printed items for places other than Philadelphia tend to be sparse. This is an area that deserves study by new researchers in the field. Judging from the many rubbings I have for manuscript volumes of Philadelphia provenance, no similar evolution in style took place for them. The three styles — panel, border and spine roll — persist in use almost interchangeably, down past the Revolution and almost into the nineteenth century. They differ from printed books in another way, in that they were very often bound in suede, not smooth leather. The traditional explanation for this is that the flesh side of the skin does not show imperfections in the leather, so that cheaper skins could be used for blankbook work. The tooling on blankbooks of this period was in blind, with no exceptions that I am aware of.

The binding styles used in New York in the early part of the eighteenth century differed in a number of ways from the styles in Boston and Philadelphia. There is something of a seventeenth-century flavor about the bindings that have been recorded, and they are easily distinguished from those of the other two cities by certain details. For example, in a panel design, whether single or double, the diagonal lines are always extended out to the corners of the boards; when a border is tooled around the four sides of a board, the decorative rolls used are considerably wider than those used in Boston and Philadelphia; and complete innovation is introduced with the use of a single fillet run down the board, parallel to the spine and two to three inches from it. (no. 12) This awkward design is one seen elsewhere only on seventeenth-century books from London stationers. Finally, New York's eighteenth-century bindings are virtually the only American ones recorded with a center stamp or medallion in the panel on the boards.

It is interesting to speculate how much these differences show the influence of a single man, William Bradford, whose New York career coincides with their use. When Bradford had his final falling out with the Quakers in Philadelphia in 1693, he moved on to New York where he became its official printer. He was then thirty years old. He would remain New York's most prominent printer for fifty years, until his retirement in 1742, and would sire a family of printer/bookbinders to follow after him. The rapid changeover from the seventeenth-century style to the binding styles common in Philadelphia took place in the 1740s, when the new generation took over the Bradford shop; this does not seem coincidental.

While Boston, Philadelphia and New York were the major sources of printing and binding in the Colonies, they were not the only ones. Every town of any size or wealth had such shops, some of them rivaling their peers in the larger cities and producing distinctive bindings worth comment. Newport, Annapolis and Williamsburg are three examples. Newport's binding trade was dominated for fifty-five years (1730 to 1785) by one man, Francis Skinner. In any location his work would have stood out. He used calf rather than sheep, highly polished and finished; he provided tooled leather jackets to cover the vellum bindings he made for local court records; and he acquired a number of unusual decorative rolls which he used on the books bound for a prominent local silversmith named John Tanner. The possibility naturally arises that the rolls may have been cut by Tanner, who was very much a bookman, and wealthy beside. Despite the imagination Skinner manifested in these differences of style and technique, he apparently saw no reason to change a successful design, for he continued to produce the double-panel design until his death in 1785.

Annapolis and Williamsburg are usually considered together, for the printer William Parks maintained his shop first in Annapolis in 1726, then in Williamsburg in 1731, and was back and forth between the two towns with great frequency. No binder has ever been named who worked in Annapolis or Williamsburg before Parks' death in 1752, but Parks must have employed binders or done some binding himself, for there are records of his having received payment for binding. The style most used in Parks' shop was the double panel, but the style is so "Scottish" as to resemble no other then in use. The bindings which have been recorded are handsome, extra-gilt morocco, the type that might be produced by a master binder in an isolated spot, who bound partly for his own pleasure, without frequent contact with current styles. Like Skinner, Parks was out of the mainstream, producing good work but paying little attention to fashion.

There are other towns along the coast and inland along the rivers where presses operated and binders worked, but none seem to have produced bindings of distinction or unusual appearance, or to have had influence on the styles of binding then in use. For example, Charleston, South Carolina, produced a Laws of South Carolina in the single-panel style, almost identical to the binding on the Laws of Pennsylvania published in Philadelphia in 1728. Not surprising, of course, for the shop in Charleston was one of Franklin's satellite operations. The New London, Connecticut, region is another example. From the introduction of printing there in 1709 until about 1780, this area was dependent on the services of a bindery which seems to have used only two hand stamps and one two-line fillet. Or so the only recorded bindings would indicate. There seems to be no explanation for this lack of binding enterprise, and little reason to expect that the area will attract a researcher into such dull and unrevealing bindings.

Let me add one last example of a distinctive early eighteenth-century style. The Pennsylvania Germans came to the New World from a culture where bookbindings were solid, sturdy and authoritative in appearance, decorated in blind with wide floral rolls and geometric patterns. The very earliest Pennsylvania German bindings were so decorated, but then there came a total about-face in the late 1730s. The decorative rolls totally disappeared from use and were replaced by single and double fillets; hand stamps disappeared as well. This was not a passing vogue or the influence of one man. Christopher Sauer is the best known practitioner of the style, but a number of other, later German binders used it as well. Even Franklin adopted it for some of his publica-

34

tions of general appeal, such as Whitefield's *Journal* (1741), Johnson's *Elementa Philosophica* (1752) and Chalkley's *Works* (1749). This striking style, so very different from any in use anywhere in the Colonies, persisted into the nineteenth century.

To recapitulate: for the first fifty to sixty years of the eighteenth century, the basic binding style in use in the American Colonies emphasized decorated boards, with little or no decoration on the spine. The 1760s would be the transitional years to a reversal in emphasis, to fancy spines and plain boards for all books except the extra-gilt category, in which the boards continued to be tooled. In the reason for this change I agree with Graham Pollard, who ascribes it to the decision to shelve books upright with their spines visible. In a paper read in 1955 to the Bibliographical Society, subsequently published in *The Library*, Pollard described the practice through the sixteenth century of shelving privately owned books in chests and presses, or displayed on tables and sloping shelves. If books were shelved, they were usually displayed with their fore-edges visible, as illustrated in numerous contemporary paintings and illustrations. This was still a time when a dozen books could constitute a private library. Then, as printing spread and produced less expensive books, collections grew. It must have become more and more difficult to select one title from the others in a group. Among the first English institutions to shelve books in the modern manner was Winchester College Library, which about 1740 made the decision to unchain its books, add titles to their spines, and shelve them with their spines visible. The new system of arrangement must have achieved instant popularity, even with private collectors. In Philadelphia there is an interesting example of the change. The books of Isaac Norris II, a wealthy eighteenth-century merchant, were changed systematically from titles lettered in ink on the fore-edge to titles lettered on the spine in 1764. Once the custom became widespread, many books would be kept standing on bookshelves, when not in use. Their covers would be invisible, and therefore there was no need to decorate them. The only exceptions would be such books as presentation copies and display pieces, somewhat similar to to-day's "coffee-table books," and blankbooks as earlier described.

A second reason for the rapid adoption of the new style of decoration, emphasizing fancy spines, was the general influx of English, Scottish and Irish binders and booksellers in the 1760s and 1770s. Such men came fully trained and at least partially equipped, and were prepared to provide the latest in fashion to the book trade. Philadelphia took in a dozen such men at least, men such as Robert Bell, Robert Aitken and Caleb Buglass. Their good Scots names appear soon after their arrival on the rolls of the St Andrew's Society. New York and Boston picked up similar groups, while individuals moved on to bind in smaller places: Londoner Thomas Brend to Annapolis, then Williamsburg and Richmond; William Poultney to Annapolis, then Baltimore and Lancaster. A number of towns added binders where none had worked before: Elizabethtown, Newark, Trenton, and Burlington in New Jersey; Wilmington, Delaware; Baltimore; Georgetown and Richmond, Virginia; Hartford and New Haven; Providence; Salem and Newburyport; Keene and Portsmouth, New Hampshire.

Despite the tension between Great Britain and the Colonies, these immigrants apparently saw golden opportunities in America, which had evolved beyond its constricted origins into a freer society. It is necessary only to scan the volumes of Evans' *American Bibliography* for the mid-eighteenth century to comprehend just how lively and literate a culture had developed. A few of the newcomers would find the Colonies un-congenial and return to the mother country, but most stayed and moved into the vacancies left by those with loyalist sympathies.

The emphasis on the spine that had begun before the Revolution continued in the postwar years. With the exception of the Pennsylvania German bindings, there were no longer any decisive regional differences, only a difference between common and more elaborate bindings. The common binding, a step-up from stitched wrappers, was plain sheep without decoration on the boards. The spine was divided into five or six compartments by a single or double fillet; the title was placed in the second compartment from the top, lettered on the spine, or on a label pasted over the compartment; if the latter, the label was outlined top and bottom by a fillet or a decorative roll. The tooling on the spine was in gold. (no. 18a) If the board edges were tooled with a decorative roll, this work was usually done in blind, and as before was quite inconspicuous. A step beyond this brings us to a more elaborate spine, produced by adding hand stamps to the center of each compartment except the title. The leather is still sheep, the end-papers still plain, the board edges still tooled in blind.

In effect, we now have a national style used on books throughout the Thirteen States, and found *en masse* in any collection of late eighteenth-century Americana. The showpieces that are extra gilt, standing out from the rest, are truly lavish in appearance. Here the bookbinder can show his stuff. Made of calf, or even morocco, with gold-tooled spines, sides, board edges and turn-ins, with marbled endpapers and title labels of colored morocco, their workmanship and appearance certainly did the new Republic proud. The library of Isaiah Thomas, now at his beloved American Antiquarian Society, is a wonderful creation of the binder's craft. Four separate workers were involved in binding these books, including the personal copies from the presses of Isaiah Thomas, New England's great merchant printer. The net effect is extraordinarily rich and impressive, and well deserves the detailed study which to my knowledge has not been made.

It is no accident that 1800 has become the cutoff date for this essay on American binding. The Industrial Revolution is just around the corner. Mechanization of many forms of work, including the cutting of binding tools, will take away clues made available by hand-made objects. And worse, the yellow-fever epidemics of 1793 and 1797 in Philadelphia will wipe out one of every six persons in that printing and binding center. As a result, many tools disappear or pass so rapidly from hand to hand that their history becomes unclear, confused.

Looking back across the intervening years to the eighteenth century, I am struck by the fact that this total change in the appearance of books was created by fashion, by a desire to change the way they looked. We are so accustomed—may I say inured—to technological change that it seems incredible to contemplate a craft in which for hundreds of years no change at all took place. It is almost soothing to consider the continuous flow of binders from one shop to another, from one generation to another; to realize that John Ratcliff of seventeenth-century Boston would have been at home in any post-Revolutionary bindery. The rules, the techniques, the tools would have been the same. He would only have had to learn to tool the spine and not the boards. I suppose he would have thought it a nonsense, and have complained about Progress.

The Bindings

A vertisement
Preface to be Ans
BALL'S Reply to On
Answer, and
COTTON'S Wo
Con..

1

38

1   A Boston Binding by John Ratcliff or Ratcliffe, ca. 1680.

Richard Mather, 1596–1669.
An Answer of the Elders of the Severall Churches in New-England unto Nine Positions.
London: Printed by T. P. and M. S. for Benjamin Allen, 1643 [and three other works: Wing A1036, T2229 and C6469].

19.2 × 15.2 × 4.1 cm.

Sheep; single-panel blind-tooled boards; blind-tooled spine fillets and board edges.

John Ratcliff came to New England from London in 1663. He is the earliest American binder for whom specific bindings can be identified. This volume, bound for Increase Mather, uses a stamp found on other Ratcliff bindings dating from 1672 through 1680 and a roll found on bindings dating between 1677 and 1684.

PROVENANCE: The first text is Richard Mather's own copy of his portion (p. 49–78) of Wing M1269 or M1270. (This text is sometimes attributed to John Davenport, but both issues in the American Antiquarian Society are attributed to Richard Mather in the hand of Increase Mather.) The second text is a presentation copy from Thomas Shepard to Richard Mather. The third text is inscribed "Liber Richardi Mather." and the fourth "I. Mather". "This book was received of Boston Athn in exchange for Ensor. Octr 23, 1828. Jos. B. Felt." and "Presented to the 'Maine Charity School' . . . by Geo. A. Thatcher. Bangor, Apr. 10. 1871."

REFERENCES: Papantonio no. 1; Hannah D. French in *Bookbinding in America* (New York, 1967), pp. 11–17; Thomas J. Holmes, American Antiquarian Society, *Proceedings,* n. s., vol. 38 (1928), pp. 31–50.

2   A Boston Binding, ca. 1718.

Samuel Lee, 1625–1691.
. . . *The Triumph of Mercy.*
Boston: B. Green for Benj. Eliot, 1718.

14.6 × 8.9 × 1.2 cm.

Sheep; single-panel blind-tooled boards; blind-tooled spine fillets.

To date, the stamp used on this binding has not been located on any other book.

PROVENANCE: Inscribed "Richard Elvin's his book", "J. B. Thornton Jr. 1851".
REFERENCE: Evans 1961.

2

3   A New York Binding from William Bradford's Shop, ca. 1722.

Conductor Generalis, or The Office, Duty and Authority of Justices of the Peace.
Philadelphia: Andrew Bradford, 1722.

19.8 × 15 × 3.7 cm.

Sheep; single-panel blind-tooled boards; blind-tooled spine fillets and board edges.

After troublesome times in Philadelphia, William Bradford moved to New York where he had his printing establishment and bindery from 1693 to 1742. In 1712 his son Andrew moved from New York back to Philadelphia where he set up a stationery shop at the "Sign of the Bible," remaining in close working relationship with his father. Though this book was printed in Philadelphia by son Andrew, it was bound in New York by his father.

PROVENANCE: Inscribed "Avis Ryersz. his Book 1736", "John Hillyer, his Book 1738", "John Hillyer his book bought of Adrianz", "John Bodine".

REFERENCE: Evans 2327.

4 A Boston Binding, ca. 1722.

Ebenezer Thayer, 1689–1733.
Christ, the Great Subject of Gospel Preaching.
Boston: S. Kneeland for S. Gerrish and D. Henchman, 1722.

16.7 × 9.8 × 3 cm.

Sheep; single-panel blind-tooled boards; blind-tooled spine fillets and board edges.

PROVENANCE: Inscribed "John Chandler's Booke Given by Deacon Brewer July 6th 1722", "Now Samuel Chandlers Book", bookplate "Ex Libris Robert R. Dearden Oaklane".
REFERENCE: Evans 2391.

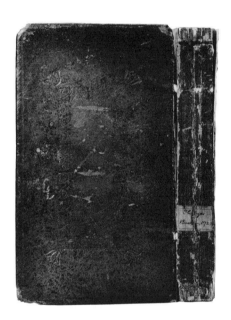

4

5 A Philadelphia Binding by William Davies, 1730.

Abel Morgan, 1673–1722.
Cyd–Gordiad Egwyddorawl o'r Scrythurau.
Philadelphia: Samuel Keimer, a Dafydd Harry, 1730.

29.7 × 18.5 × 2.6 cm.

Sheep; double-panel blind-tooled boards; blind-tooled board edges; rebacked.

The Quaker William Davies was born in the Colony of Pennsylvania in 1693. He was binding by 1721. Moving to Philadelphia in 1726, he continued binding there until his death in 1740. This Welsh concordance is the earliest Bible concordance printed in America.

PROVENANCE: Inscribed "Owen Evans . . . 1730".
REFERENCE: Evans 3303.

5

6 A Boston Binding, ca. 1731.

Matthew Henry, 1662–1714.
The Communicant's Companion. Tenth edition.
Boston: Reprinted for S. Kneeland, 1731.

16.5 × 10.4 × 2.9 cm.

Sheep; single-panel blind-tooled boards; blind-tooled spine fillets and board edges.

PROVENANCE: Inscribed "William Tarbox's Book. Given to him by Joanna Smith in the year 1793", "Thomas Fleet His Book".
REFERENCE: cf. Evans 3429, imprint variant.

7   A Boston Binding, ca. 1740.

William Cooper, 1694–1743.
The Doctrine of Predestination unto Life.
Boston: J. Draper for J. Edwards and H. Foster, 1740.

16.2 × 10.4 × 2.1 cm.

Sheep; blind-tooled boards, spine fillets and board edges.

PROVENANCE: Inscribed "John Staniford 1740".

REFERENCE: Evans 4497.

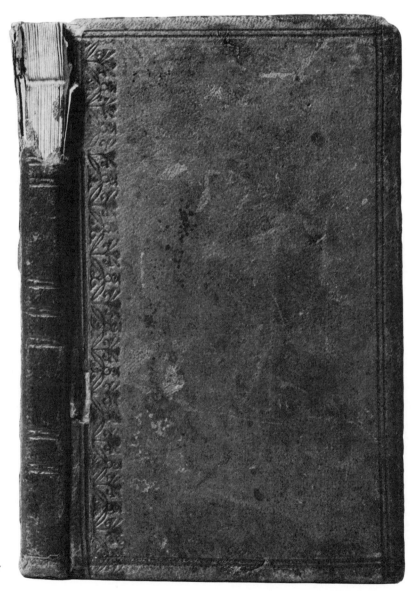

7

8   A Boston Binding, ca. 1747.

The American Magazine.
[Boston, January–December 1746.]

21.3 × 15.8 × 3.8 cm.

Sheep; blind-tooled boards with double panel in contrasting brown, blind-tooled spine fillets
and turn-ins.

PROVENANCE: Inscribed "Wm Winthrop".

REFERENCE: Evans 5728.

8

9 An Ephrata Cloister Binding, ca. 1754.

John Bunyan, 1628–1688.
Eines Christen Reise.
Ephrata: Drucks und Verlags der Bruderschafft, 1754.

16.8 × 11.4 × 4.3 cm.

Calf; brass clasp from back board, with heart-shaped hook and hinge plates.

Though first using the elaborate decorative binding tools they had brought with them from Europe, the early German and Swiss binders of Pennsylvania soon developed a plain style in keeping with their faith and reminiscent of the most simple late-medieval bindings. The binding on this book is typical of the Cloister's work, but the heart-shaped clasp is unusual. Clasps on Pennsylvania German books, like their Germanic prototypes, are attached to the back board and hook on the front board.

PROVENANCE: "T.C." (initials on clasp), inscribed "Tobias Stauffer . . . 1829".

REFERENCES: Evans 7162 and 7163; Hazel Dreis, "Lancaster, Pennsylvania, Bookbindings: An Historical Survey," The Bibliographical Society of America, *Papers,* vol. 42 (1948), pp. 119–128. (Though the only substantial study of Pennsylvania German bindings published to date, this article includes numerous assumptions and conclusions with which the editors of this publication do not agree.)

9

10   A Boston Binding, 1762.

Joseph Bellamy, 1719-1790.
An Essay on the Nature and Glory of the Gospel.
Boston: S. Kneeland, 1762.

16.8 × 10.9 × 2.5 cm.

Sheep; gilt-tooled spine fillets, with red morocco title label; blind-tooled board edges.

The first New England spine label is said to have been used for Samuel Willard's *Divinity* of 1726 (also in the Maser Collection). After 1740 they became more frequent in New England, though they were uncommon in Philadelphia for much of the century.

PROVENANCE: Inscribed "Ann Lowder 1762".

REFERENCE: Evans 9064.

10

11 A Philadelphia Binding Attributed to George Christopher Reinholdt, ca. 1763.

Henrich Funck, d. 1760.
Eine Restitution.
Philadelphia: Gedruckt bey Anton Armbrüster in Moravien Ally, 1763.

21.5 × 17.1 × 4.2 cm.

Sheep; blind-tooled fillets along the inner edge of the boards and also spine fillets; leather strapwork added later along the top and bottom of spine and boards, together with small leather studs centered on both boards, all held in place with small square copper bosses.

In 1753, at the age of thirty, George Christopher Reinholdt sailed to Pennsylvania from Germany, where he had his initial training. In 1763 he set up his own bindery in Philadelphia, where he continued to work until his death in 1793. This simple sheep binding was later turned into a more unusual binding by the addition of crude strapwork and copper bosses. Though the intention of the additions may have been in part decorative, they were largely designed to strengthen and preserve the original binding.

PROVENANCE: Inscribed "John Bear", "Jacob Pegner", "Frau Ja Baumanni zu E E Anno 1775", "Marry Baumanni", "Christian Bauman".

REFERENCE: Evans 9393.

11

12   A New York Binding, ca. 1768.

Giles Jacob, 1686–1744.
Every Man His Own Lawyer. Seventh edition.
New York: Hugh Gaine, 1768.

19.7 × 12.8 × 2.7 cm.

Sheep; blind-tooled boards.

PROVENANCE: Bookseller's label of John Dunlap inside front cover, inscribed "James Turnbull Esq the year 1786", "George Turnbull his Book 1789", "Jno. Ingram".

REFERENCE: Evans 10935.

12

13 A New York Binding, ca. 1773.

Girolamo Zanchi, 1516?–1590.
The Doctrine of Absolute Predestination Stated and Asserted.
New York: Hodge and Shober for Samuel Loudon, 1773.

16.7 × 10.5 × 1.8 cm.

Sheep; blind-tooled boards.

PROVENANCE: Inscribed "John Bingham Junr His Book 1769", "John Bingham, Senr 1770".
REFERENCE: Evans 13089.

13

14 A Germantown, Pennsylvania, Binding from Christopher Sauer's Shop, ca. 1776.

Bible. German.
Biblia, das ist: Die ganze Göttliche Heilige Schrift.
Germantown: Gedruckt und zu finden bey Christoph Saur, 1776.

26.1 × 22.1 × 9.4 cm.

Pigskin on beveled wooden boards; blind-tooled boards and spine fillets; two brass clasps on leather straps from back board; leather strapwork with nailhead bosses at head and tail of spine, as well as brass corner and center bosses, added later.

The use of pigskin is rare on Pennsylvania German bindings, though it was common in Germany itself. The decorative panels, which have their outer panels stained, are more ornamental than the plain boards which usually emanated from Sauer's shop. The bosses and strapwork were added later to strengthen the original binding. The fine workmanship of the original clasps compares interestingly with the later brasswork.

The text of the work is also of interest in the history of American printing, for it was the first German Bible to be printed in America from American cast type.

REFERENCE: Evans 14663.

14

15 A Philadelphia County Binding by Christopher Hoffmann, ca. 1784.

Christopher Schultz, 1718–1789.
Kurze Fragen ueber die Christliche Glaubens-Lehre.
Philadelphia: Gedruckt bey Carl Cist, 1784.

16.7 × 10.4 × 1.6 cm.

Sprinkled calf; blind-tooled boards and spine fillets; red sprinkled edges.

Christopher Hoffmann (1727–1804) was a Schwenckfelder minister as well as an accomplished binder. He lived in Lower Salford Township where he flourished from the early 1760s until his death. In design his tools appear to have come from Ireland. This small catechism bears one of his distinctive rolls, together with simple fillets on both boards.

REFERENCE: Evans 18779.

15

16a A Philadelphia County Binding by Christopher Hoffmann, ca. 1791.

Erasmus Weichenhan, d. 1594.
Christliche Betrachtungen.
Germantown: Gedruckt bey Michael Billmeyer, 1791.

22 × 18.1 × 5.7 cm.

Calf on beveled wooden boards; paneled blind-tooled boards and spine fillets; brass clasps on leather straps from back board; red-stained edges.

Pennsylvania German bindings with beveled wooden boards have the beveling on the inside edges of the boards rather than on the outside edges. When using wooden boards, Hoffmann followed this tradition.

REFERENCE: Evans 23975.

16a

16b   A Philadelphia County Binding by Christopher Hoffmann, ca. 1762.

Neu-Eingerichtetes Gesang-Buch.
Germantown: Gedruckt bey Christoph Saur, 1762.

18.9 × 13 × 5.5 cm.

Calf on beveled wooden boards; paneled blind-tooled boards; blind-tooled spine; brass nailhead bosses on corners of boards; brass clasps on leather straps from back board; marbled endpapers; red-stained edges; clasp-straps repaired.

This copy of the first Schwenkfelder hymn book has manuscript notes and indexes by Christopher Hoffmann, who was a hymnologist as well as a clergyman and a bookbinder.

REFERENCES: Evans 9266; Papantonio no. 9; Allen Anders Seipt, *Schwenkfelder Hymnology* (Philadelphia, 1909).

17   A Philadelphia Binding by Robert Aitken's Shop, 1799.

Bible. English.
The Holy Bible.
Philadelphia: Printed for John Thompson & Abraham Small, 1798.

43 × 27.5 × 6.5 cm., 2 volumes.

Red morocco with black morocco title labels and green morocco volume labels; gilt-tooled boards, spines, board edges and turn-ins; marbled endpapers; all edges gilt.

ILLUSTRATED IN COLOR AS FRONTISPIECE.

The work of the shop of Robert Aitken (1735–1802), Philadelphia printer and binder from 1771 to 1802, is the best documented of all early American houses. There Jane Aitken, daughter and successor of Robert, received her training. After her father's death in 1802, she gained distinction in her own right as printer, binder and bookseller. The style of her tooling, in contrast to that of her father, seems evident in this elegant binding. The Aitkens and their work are detailed most fully in the article by Willman and Carol Spawn. Their article also pictures and describes the significance of this superb copy of the Thompson and Small "Hot Press" Bible.

PROVENANCE: Inscribed "Isaac Harvey Jr", "Bt of Leary. May 1904."

REFERENCES: Evans 33408; Willman and Carol Spawn, "The Aitken Shop," The Bibliographical Society of America, *Papers*, vol. 57 (1963), pp. 422–437; Carol M. Spawn, "Jane Aitken," *Notable American Women, 1607–1950* (Cambridge, Massachusetts, 1971).

A detail from the front board of volume one.

18a   A Philadelphia Binding, ca. 1793.

Bible. O. T. Psalms.
Psalms, Carefully Suited to the Christian Worship.
Philadelphia: W. Young, 1793.

9.7 × 6 × 2.1 cm.

Sprinkled calf with red morocco title label; gilt-tooled spine fillets.

William Young, the publisher of these volumes, also advertised as a binder. It is not known if he bound these two copies of his Psalter though the forwarding of the two volumes is very similar. It was common to provide religious service books in a variety of bindings, depending on taste and cost.

PROVENANCE: Inscribed "Joel Westcott's Psalm Book 1796".
REFERENCE: Evans 25180.

18b   A Philadelphia Binding, ca. 1793.

Bible. O. T. Psalms.
Psalms, Carefully Suited to the Christian Worship.
Philadelphia: W. Young, 1793.

9.4 × 6 × 2.2 cm.

Calf with black morocco title label; gilt-tooled boards, spine and board edges; marbled end-papers; yellow-stained edges.

PROVENANCE: Inscribed "George W. Janvier's", "This Book, Presented by my father in or near the year one thousand seven hundred and ninety four, I present to my Mary. Aug. 29. 1844. G. W. Janvier".
REFERENCE: Evans 25180.

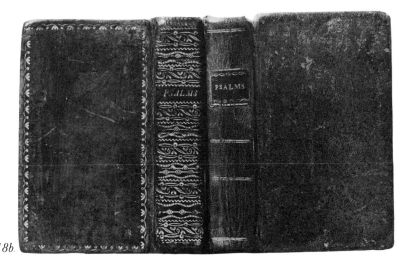

18b   *18a*

19　A New York Binding, ca. 1796.

Reformed Dutch Church in North America.
The Psalms of David, with Hymns and Spiritual Songs.
New York: G. Forman for S. Campbell, 1796.

17 × 10.4 × 3.9 cm.

Red morocco; gilt-tooled boards, gilt-lettered and tooled spine and board edges; marbled end-papers; "John Kane." stamped horizontally in gilt on front cover.

PROVENANCE: "John Kane."

REFERENCE: Evans 30071.

19

20   A New York Binding, ca. 1800.

Hannah More, 1745–1833.
Strictures on the Modern System of Female Education.
Philadelphia: Budd and Bartram for Thomas Dobson, 1800.

17.9 × 11.4 × 2.2 cm., 2 volumes.

Tree calf with red morocco title labels and green morocco volume labels; gilt-tooled spines and board edges.

REFERENCE: Evans 37996.

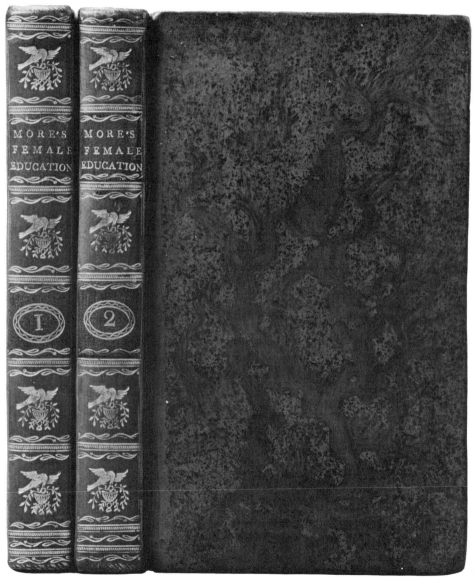

20

21

21   A Boston Binding by Henry Bilson Legge, ca. 1801.

Jeremy Belknap, 1744–1798.
Sacred Poetry, Consisting of Psalms and Hymns. Third edition.
Boston: Printed for Thomas & Andrews and West & Greenleaf, 1801.

15 × 9.3 × 2.3 cm.

Green morocco; gilt-tooled boards, spine, board edges and turn-ins; marbled endpapers; all edges gilt.

Henry Bilson Legge (1763–1804) came to New England after "much experience in London." His name appears in Boston directories between 1798 and 1803, though he may have worked elsewhere in the States before that. In addition to the handsomely tooled bindings he produced, he greatly influenced the Boston binder John Roulstone, who came into possession of many of Legge's tools after his death.

PROVENANCE: Inscribed "Ephm H. Farrar's January 1st. 1845."

REFERENCES: Shaw & Shoemaker 156; Hannah D. French, "Bound in Boston by Henry B. Legg," The Bibliographical Society of the University of Virginia, *Studies in Bibliography, Papers,* vol. 17 (1964), pp. 135–139.

22   A Boston Binding by Henry Bilson Legge, ca. 1802.

Psalms, Hymns, and Spiritual Songs: Selected and Designed for the Use of the Church Universal.
Boston: Munroe & Francis, 1802.

17 × 10.6 × 3.2 cm.

Tree calf; gilt-tooled boards, spine and board edges; marbled endpapers; "N. Johnston."
stamped vertically in gilt on front cover.

PROVENANCE: Inscribed "Ira B. Hoitt East Northwood NH 1819", "N. Johnston."
REFERENCE: Shaw & Shoemaker 3453.

22

23   A Lancaster, Pennsylvania, Binding, 1802.

The Washingtoniana.
Lancaster: William Hamilton, 1802.

21.7 × 13.5 × 3 cm.

Calf, with black morocco title label; gilt-tooled boards, spine, board edges and turn-ins; marbled endpapers.

The anonymous binder of this work was also the binder for the Pennsylvania Assembly Library in Harrisburg.

PROVENANCE: Inscribed "Thomas Wentz his Book Bought March The Twenty Eight One Thousand Eight Hundred and Two", "Presented to Thomas J. Wentz By his Mother 1841".

REFERENCE: Shaw & Shoemaker 3496.

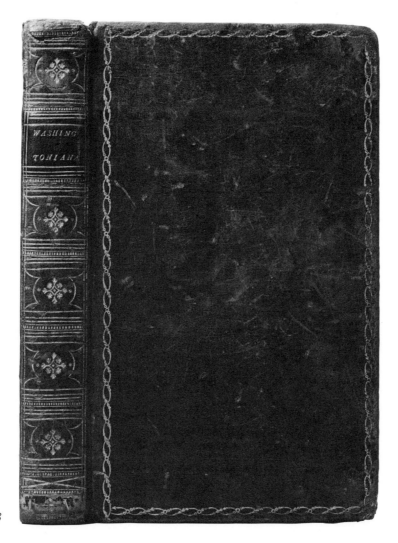

23

24a A New York Binding by William Swaim, ca. 1807.

Edmund Burke, 1729–1797.
The Works.
Boston: John West and O. C. Greenleaf, 1806–1807. David Carlisle, Printer. (Volumes 1–4).

22.6 × 14.5 × 3.6 cm., 4 volumes.

Acid-stained calf with black leather title and volume labels; gilt-tooled boards, spine, board edges and turn-ins; marbled endpapers; sprinkled yellow-stained edges.

"Swaim" stamped in gilt on upper right vertical turn-in of front boards.

William Swaim first appears in Longworth's New York directory in 1805, the same year he won the prize for the best American binding in American leather at the Literary Fair of the American Company of Booksellers held in Newark, New Jersey. The award-winning binding is very similar to this work, including the "American leather." Swaim's name continues to appear in the directories through 1817.

PROVENANCE: Bookplate of "Max Freedman".
REFERENCES: Shaw & Shoemaker 10067; Hannah D. French, "Notes on American Bookbindings: The Award-winning Binding of William Swaim," American Antiquarian Society, *Proceedings*, vol. 91 (1981), pp. 325–327.

24b A New York Binding, ca. 1813.

Edmund Burke, 1729–1797.
The Works.
New York: Eastburn, Kirk and Co. and West and Richardson, and Oliver C. Greenleaf, Boston, 1813. C. S. Van Winkle, Printer. (Volumes 5–6).

22.6 × 14.5 × 4.2 cm., 2 volumes.

Acid-stained calf with morocco title and volume labels; gilt-tooled boards, spine, board edges and turn-ins; marbled endpapers; sprinkled yellow-stained edges.

This pair of unsigned bindings was designed to duplicate the bindings executed by Swaim about five years earlier. Though the individual tools differ from Swaim's, the effect is very similar.

PROVENANCE: Bookplate of "Max Freedman".
REFERENCE: Shaw & Shoemaker 28047.

64

24a

24b

25 A New York Binding by Eliza Culley, ca. 1808.

Elizabeth Rowe, 1674–1737.
Devout Exercises of the Heart.
[bound with] Imitatio Christi. English.
An Extract of the Christian's Pattern.
New York: Ezekiel Cooper and John Wilson for the Methodist Connection in the United States, J. C. Totten, Printer, 1808.

10.6 × 6.5 × 3 cm.

Red roan with black morocco title label; gilt-tooled boards, spine, board edges and turn-ins; marbled endpapers; all edges gilt.

"Eliza Culley" stamped in blind on foot of spine.

"Widow Eliza Culley" had been married to the shoemaker John Culley. No doubt she learned about leathers and stitching in helping him at his trade. It is only after his death that the New York directories eventually number her among the bookbinders. The directories first list her in her own right in 1807/8, and she last appears in 1828. Another John, presumably her son, appears at her address as a printer in 1822/23.

PROVENANCE: Bookplate of "Genevieve Ludlow Griscom".
REFERENCE: Shaw & Shoemaker 16104 (includes 15292).

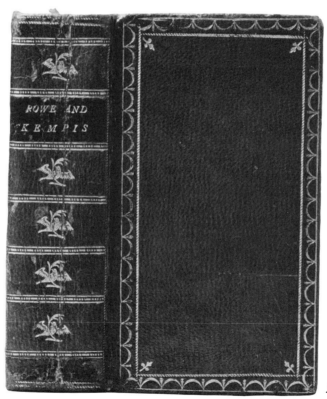

25

26 A Lancaster, Pennsylvania, Binding, ca. 1810.

John Wesley, 1703–1791.
A Survey of the Wisdom of God in the Creation.
Lancaster: William Hamilton, 1810.

21.9 × 13.7 × 3.9 cm., 2 volumes.

Tree calf; gilt-tooled boards, gilt-lettered and tooled spines, blind-stamped board edges and turn-ins; marbled endpapers.

PROVENANCE: Bookseller's label of "Hurst's Second Hand Books . . . Lancaster, Pa."
REFERENCE: Shaw & Shoemaker 22018.

26

27 A Philadelphia Binding, ca. 1812.

The Freemason's Magazine and General Miscellany.
Philadelphia: Levis & Weaver, 1811–1812.

20.9 × 13.6 × 3.8 cm., 2 volumes.

Acid stained leather with black morocco title labels and brown oval onlays with volume number; gilt- and blind-tooled boards, gilt-tooled spines, board edges and turn-ins; marbled endpapers.

Unfortunately only two years of this journal were published, for it importantly chronicled Freemasonry at the time. The handsome acid-stained or "Spanish leather" binding was gilt- and blind-tooled with rolls common to binders working in all the major centers of the trade. Though calf skins could be purchased already acid stained, many binders created their own patterns by the varied mixtures of acid washes used on the leather. To prevent rotting of the leather, it was critical that the acid was immediately washed off the skin after the stained effect was achieved.

PROVENANCE: Bookstamp of "Geo. T. DaCosta.", bookplate of "Dr. J. Chalmers DaCosta".
REFERENCE: Shaw & Shoemaker 22873.

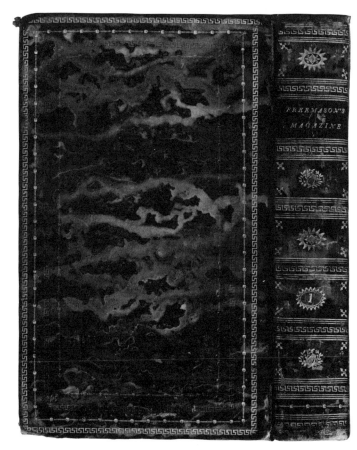

27

28   An Exeter, New Hampshire, Binding by Francis Grant, ca. 1816.

Philip Doddridge, 1702–1751.
The Family Expositor.
Boston: Etheridge and Bliss, 1807–08.

22.5 × 14.5 × 3.5 cm., 6 volumes.

Green roan; gilt-tooled boards, spines, board edges and turn-ins; green endpapers; yellow-stained edges.

Binder's label inside front covers of volumes 2, 4 and 6.

A lifetime Exeter resident, Francis Grant (1792–1865) began his professional career as a bookbinder. He possibly learned the rudiments of the art under the tutelage of John Sawyer, a simple binder working with the Exeter printer Charles Norris. The earliest located signed bindings by Grant are on *The Laws of the State of New Hampshire,* printed by Norris in 1815. Though these are simple calf bindings, more elaborate and more skillful work soon followed. In 1820 he embarked on a publishing career and no signed bindings after this date have been located. In addition Grant maintained a new and used bookshop where he also took in binding until he sold the bindery to Gilman Rand in 1856.

PROVENANCE: Inscribed "C. H. Orne to Mrs H. Ropes."
REFERENCE: Shaw & Shoemaker 12446.

70

28

29 A New York Binding, ca. 1817.

Protestant Episcopal Church.
The Book of Common Prayer.
New York: W. B. Gilley, 1817.

11.4 × 7.4 × 3.4 cm.

Black roan; gilt-tooled and blind-stamped boards, gilt-lettered and tooled spine, board edges
and turn-ins; marbled endpapers; all edges gilt; "M. Carvill" stamped vertically in gilt on front
cover.

PROVENANCE: "M. Carvill", inscribed "Thomas Hulme".

REFERENCE: Shaw & Shoemaker 41895.

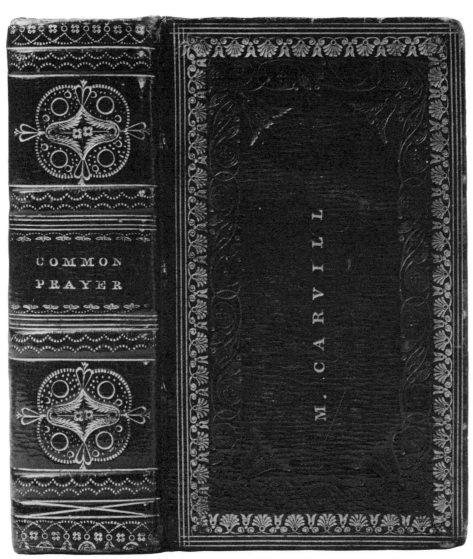

29

71

30 A New York Binding Attributed to Henry I. Megarey, ca. 1819.

Protestant Episcopal Church.
The Book of Common Prayer.
New York: Henry I. Megarey, 1819.
[bound with] Bible. O. T. Psalms.
The Whole Book of Psalms.
New York: Henry I. Megarey, 1819.

25 × 15.5 × 4.6 cm.

Red straight-grained morocco; gilt- and blind-tooled boards and spine; gilt-lettered spine; gilt-tooled board edges; rose paper doublures, bordered by gilt-tooling to match boards; all edges gilt with border gauffering.

ILLUSTRATED IN COLOR AS PLATE I FOLLOWING P. 17.

MEGAREY'S *Book of Common Prayer* has received accolades for its overall design and typography. Andrews wrote: "The letter, the justification, the register, the ink, and the press-work are of the best kind. . . ." Several copies of the book, bound at the shop of Megarey, are known from ticketed examples. This copy is attributed to Megarey on the basis of common tools used in ticketed volumes.

PROVENANCE: Gilt-tooled leather bookplate lettered "Anna D. Perkins." on inside front cover.
REFERENCES: Shaw & Shoemaker 49199 (includes 47346); Papantonio no. 39; William Loring Andrews, *Bibliopegy in the United States and Kindred Subjects* (New York, 1902), pp. 9–15.

31 An Ephrata, Pennsylvania, Binding, ca. 1820.

Ezekiel Sangmeister, 1724–1785?
Mystische Theologie.
Ephrata: Gedruckt und zu haben bey Joseph Bauman, 1819–20.

16.9 × 10.3 × 2 cm.

Quarter calf; printed paper boards; blind-tooled spine fillets.

Though bindings of decorative paper had been used occasionally elsewhere in the States and at earlier dates, they had wide popularity among the Pennsylvania Germans, particularly between 1810 and 1840.

PROVENANCE: Inscribed "Jacob Bär sein Buch May 22. 1842".
REFERENCES: Shaw & Shoemaker 49359, Shoemaker 3107.

32 A Lancaster, Pennsylvania, Binding, ca. 1821.

Bible. N. T. German.
Das Neue Testament.
Lancaster: Gedruckt bey Johann Bär, 1821.

18.7 × 11.3 × 4.1 cm.

Calf on beveled wooden boards; tin corner and center bosses with brass nailheads; strapwork at head and tail of spine; brass clasps on leather straps from back board.

The tin corner and center bosses are somewhat cruder than the brass of the clasps and may have been added to the binding, together with the strapwork, after it was completed.

PROVENANCE: Inscribed "Das buch gehoert mir Johannes Jotter im Jahr, 1826".
REFERENCE: Shoemaker 4684.

32

33a   *33b*

33a   An Exeter, New Hampshire, Binding, ca. 1822.

Bible. O. T. Psalms.
The Psalms of David, imitated . . . by Isaac Watts.
Exeter, New Hampshire: John I. Williams, 1822.

9.8 × 6 × 3 cm.

Red roan; gilt-tooled boards and board edges; gilt-lettered and tooled spine; yellow-stained edges.

These Exeter bindings are among a small group of fine bindings using overlapping tools. Benjamin J. Williams, the brother and partner of publisher John J. Williams, was a binder and may have bound these Psalters.

PROVENANCE: Inscribed "Miss Catharine Clay, Chester, N.H.", "I.W.L."
REFERENCE: Shoemaker 8041.

33b   An Exeter, New Hampshire, Binding, ca. 1822.

Bible. O. T. Psalms.
The Psalms of David, imitated . . . by Isaac Watts.
Exeter, New Hampshire: John I. Williams, 1822.

9.8 × 6 × 3 cm.

Red roan; gilt-tooled boards and board edges; gilt-lettered and tooled spine; "James Tallant" stamped vertically in gilt on front cover.

PROVENANCE: "James Tallant".
REFERENCE: Shoemaker 8041.

34   A Boston Binding, ca. 1823.

Henry Kirke White, 1785–1806.
The Remains of Henry Kirke White, of Nottingham.
Boston: Timothy Bedlington, 1823. [Blake, Cutler & Co., Printers, Bellows Falls, Vt.]

15.1 × 9.4 × 2.2 cm., 2 volumes.

Acid-stained calf with red morocco title labels and black morocco volume labels; gilt-tooled boards, spines, edges and turn-ins; marbled endpapers; yellow-stained edges.

PROVENANCE: Inscribed "Mary M. Kent, Amherst", "E. Spalding from his cousin M.K."
REFERENCE: Shoemaker 14893.

35a   A Philadelphia Binding, ca. 1823.

Thomas Gisborne, 1758–1846.
The Testimony of Natural Theology to Christianity.
Philadelphia: Published by M. Thomas, T. H. Palmer, Printer, 1818.

18.9 × 11.3 × 2.2 cm.

Sprinkled calf; morocco skiver spine, gilt-tooled and lettered; yellow-stained edges.

These anonymous bindings, though bound in calf, were designed to look like more elegant black morocco bindings when placed in a bookcase. The thin skivered leather on the spines was applied to the full calf bindings as though they were title labels.

PROVENANCE: Inscribed "Edward Smith 1823", bookstamps of "Benjamin Archer" and "Salem Library".
REFERENCE: Shaw & Shoemaker 44163.

35b   A Philadelphia Binding, ca. 1823.

Christoph Christian Sturm, 1740–1786.
Reflections on the Works of God.
Philadelphia: Hickman & Hazzard, 1821.

19 × 11.1 × 2.7 (vol. 1), 3.2 (vol. 2) cm., 2 volumes.

Sprinkled calf; morocco skiver spines, gilt-tooled and lettered; yellow-stained edges.

PROVENANCE: Bookstamps of "Benjamin Archer" and "Salem Library".
REFERENCE: Shoemaker 6916.

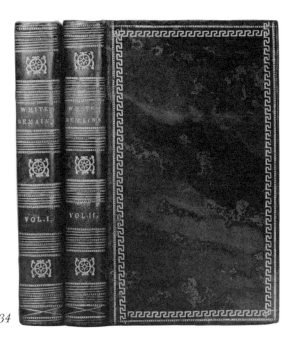

34

35b   35a

77

36 A Reading, Pennsylvania, Binding by Christian Koch, ca. 1824.

Bible. N. T. German.
Das Neue Testament.
Carlisle: Gedruckt und zu haben bey Moser und Peters, 1824.

17.5 × 11 × 4.1 cm.

Calf on beveled wooden boards; blind-tooled boards and spine fillets; mottled calf turn-ins; brass clasps on blind-tooled leather straps from back board; upper hinge repaired.

Binder's label inside front cover (see below).

Binder's tickets are exceedingly rare in Pennsylvania German bindings. The bindings of Christopher Hoffmann (15 and 16a & b) have been identified by a comparison of tools he used on bindings for which the Schwenkfelder Archives indicate the binder.

PROVENANCE: Inscribed "Isaac Krick 1857 In Spring Township Berks County Pensilvania".
REFERENCE: Shoemaker 15365.

36

37 A New York Binding Possibly by Wilson & Nichols, ca. 1826.

Bible. English.
The Holy Bible.
New York: Stereotyped by A. Chandler for the American Bible Society, 1826.

14 × 8.7 × 4 cm.

Red straight-grained morocco; gilt- and blind-tooled boards; gilt-lettered and tooled spine, board edges and turn-ins; marbled endpapers; "W. C. Redfield." stamped vertically in gilt on front cover.

Wilson & Nichols gained distinction in the binding of the numerous presentation copies of C. D. Colden's lavish 1825 memoir on the New York canals. On the basis of both the style and the use of matching tools (see Andrews, *Bibliopegy,* p. 98 and Papantonio no. 47), this binding is tentatively attributed to that firm.

PROVENANCE: "W. C. Redfield."

REFERENCES: Shoemaker 23776; Willman Spawn, "Notes on American Bookbindings: Wilson & Nichols Bindings," American Antiquarian Society, *Proceedings,* vol. 90 (1980), pp. 235–236.

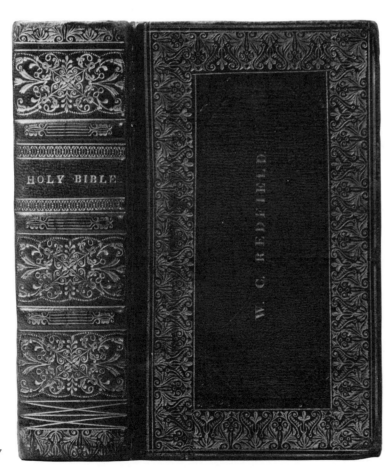

37

38

38   An Exeter, New Hampshire, Binding by Benjamin J. Williams, ca. 1828.

Sir Walter Scott, 1771–1832.
The Life of Napoleon Buonaparte.
Exeter: J. & B. Williams, 1828.

21.9 × 13.5 × 4.1 cm., 2 volumes.

Black roan; gilt-tooled boards and board edges; gilt-lettered and tooled spines.

Benjamin J. Williams bound large numbers of books with the "J. & B. Williams" imprint. The sets of Scott's *Napoleon* compared with this copy all reveal the same overall design but with the small variations typical of hand-binding as it moved toward mass production.

PROVENANCE: Inscribed "Chas. Stearns" in volume 2.

REFERENCE: Shoemaker 35122.

39   A New York Binding Attributed to Nathaniel B. Holmes, ca. 1828.

Robert Pollok, 1798–1827.
The Course of Time.
Boston: Crocker and Brewster; New York: J. Leavitt, 1828.

18.1 × 11.4 × 2.5 cm.

Calf; gilt- and blind-tooled boards; gilt-lettered and tooled spine; gilt board edges and turn-ins; marbled endpapers; all edges stained.

Though this binding is unsigned, it is marked by the style of New York binder Nathaniel B. Holmes. A ticketed Holmes binding in the Papantonio Collection at the American Antiquarian Society also bears some duplication of tools. Holmes, who is listed in the New York directories from 1819 through 1836, was elected to the New York Friendly Association of Master Book-Binders in 1822.

PROVENANCE: Inscribed "Mrs. Parmly, from her respectful Friend, E. Adams New York Oct. 28th 1831."

REFERENCE: Shoemaker 34830.

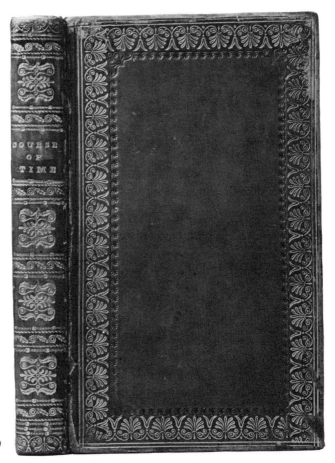

39

40a   A Philadelphia Binding, ca. 1829.

Reformed Dutch Church in North America.
The Psalms and Hymns.
Philadelphia: G. W. Mentz, 1829.

15.2 × 9.4 × 3.5 cm.

Red crushed morocco; gilt- and blind-tooled boards; gilt-tooled spine, board edges and turn-ins; marbled endpapers; all edges gilt; "Margaret Foering" stamped horizontally in gilt on front cover.

These two volumes present interesting examples of variant super-gilt-extra bindings, executed by the same shop for two copies of the same book.

PROVENANCE: "Margaret Foering".
REFERENCE: Shoemaker 40228.

40b   A Philadelphia Binding, ca. 1829.

Reformed Dutch Church in North America.
The Psalms and Hymns.
Philadelphia: G. W. Mentz, 1829.

15.2 × 9.5 × 3.4 cm.

Red crushed morocco; gilt- and blind-stamped boards; gilt-tooled spine, board edges and turn-ins; marbled endpapers; all edges gilt.

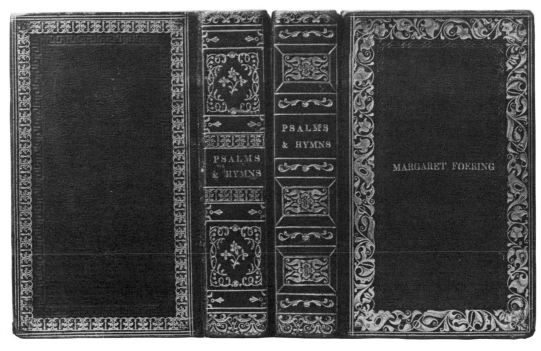

40b   *40a*

41   A New York Binding, ca. 1829.

Methodist Episcopal Church.
A Collection of Hymns.
New York: J. Emory and B. Waugh for the Methodist Episcopal Church, 1829.

9.1 × 5.9 × 2.5 cm.

Red crushed morocco; gilt- and blind-stamped boards, spine and flap; marbled endpapers; all edges gilt; "Catharine Ann Plaskitt" stamped vertically in gilt on flap.

Pocketbook bindings were occasionally used for small dictionaries but most frequently for church books of various sorts.

PROVENANCE: "Catharine Ann Plaskitt".
REFERENCE: Shoemaker 39569.

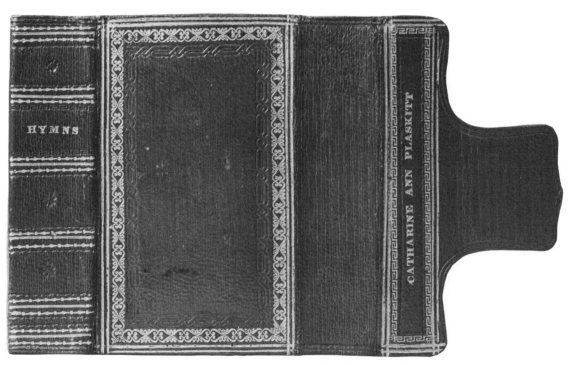

41

42   A Baltimore Binding of the 1830s.

Thomas Campbell, 1777–1844.
The Poetical Works.
Baltimore: P. N. Wood [n.d.].

10.5 × 7 × 2.5 cm.

Calf; gilt- and blind-tooled boards, gilt-lettered and tooled spine, gilt board edges and turn-ins; marbled endpapers; all edges gilt.

PROVENANCE: Inscribed "Louisa M Brown" and "Elton".

REFERENCE: A possible variant of item 18096 in *A Checklist of American Imprints for 1833* (Metuchen, New Jersey, 1979).

42

43a A Philadelphia Binding by Benjamin Gaskill, ca. 1837.

James Herring, 1794–1867, ed.
The National Portrait Gallery of Distinguished Americans.
Philadelphia: Henry Perkins, 1835–1836.

27.6 × 18.8 × 3.8 cm., 3 volumes (Half-titles and spines dated 1834, 1835, 1836).

Black morocco; embossed-panel boards and spines with gilt-tooled borders and spine labels; gilt-tooled edges and turn-ins; glossy yellow endpapers.

Embossed bindings first appeared in England about 1827, developing further the popular blocked bindings. Blocked bindings were usually created in a standing or arming press where the leather of the already bound book was impressed with the design of the block. Embossed bindings were created in a huge fly-embossing press where the cover alone was embossed with the design of both a brass die and a brass counter die. This latter method was first perfected by the embossing of paper. The technique was popularized in England by the firm of Remnant & Edmonds, whose early work is also represented in the Maser Collection.

In America the technique was picked up and developed by Benjamin Gaskill of Philadelphia. Working as a binder between 1809 and 1855, he and his sons popularized the embossed binding. Benjamin Jr became the engraver of binders' tools and plaques and his father and brother Edward remained binders. The embossed spine on this set is copied from a Remnant & Edmonds spine plaque, attesting to the interrelatedness of American and British binders of the period.

PROVENANCE: Inscribed "Mrs W. H. Jackson."

REFERENCES: Eleanore Jamieson, *English Embossed Bindings, 1825–1850* (Cambridge, 1972); Edwin Wolf 2nd in *The Annual Report of the Library Company of Philadelphia for the Year 1977* (1978), pp. 22–27.

43b A Philadelphia Binding by Benjamin Gaskill, ca. 1839.

James Herring, 1794–1867, ed.
The National Portrait Gallery of Distinguished Americans.
Philadelphia: Henry Perkins, 1835–1839.

29 × 24.2 × 4.1 cm., 4 volumes (Half-titles and spines dated 1834, 1835, 1836, 1839).

Black morocco with maroon morocco title labels; embossed-panel boards with gilt- and blind-tooled borders; gilt-tooled spines, board edges, and turn-ins; glossy yellow endpapers.

This large paper copy of *The National Portrait Gallery* has a fully gilt-tooled spine, in contrast to the use of the panel plaque on the smaller set. The tooling on the boards further distinguishes the two copies.

PROVENANCE: Booklabel of Brian Douglas Stilwell.

43a

86

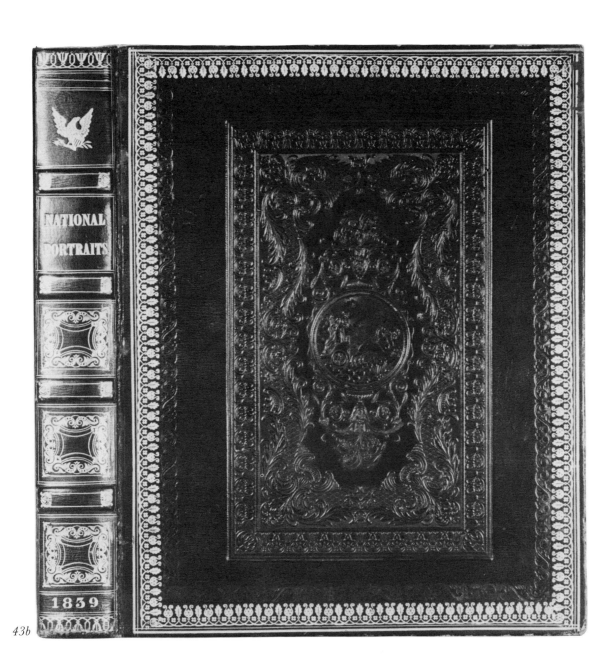

43b

44 A Chambersburg, Pennsylvania, Binding for the Publication Office of the German Reformed Church, ca. 1842.

German Reformed Church.
Liturgy for the Use of the Congregation.
Chambersburg, Pennsylvania: Printed at the Publication Office, 1841.
[bound with] *Liturgie, oder Kirchen-Formular, der Hochdeutsch Reformirten Kirche.*
Chambersburg, Pennsylvania: In der Druckerei der Reformirten Kirche, 1842.

14.8 × 10.4 × 1.9 cm.

Red morocco; gilt-tooled boards and spine; gilt-lettered spine; marbled endpapers; all edges gilt.

ILLUSTRATED IN COLOR AS PLATE II FOLLOWING p. 17.

In Chambersburg, through various publishing houses, the Reformed Church issued its publications from 1835 until 1864 when the town was burned by the Confederates in retaliation for Northern depredations in the South. In 1843 the Church Publication Office purchased a bindery, which began operation in April 1844. Prior to this date books and pamphlets were sent out to be bound, some to Harrisburg, some to Hagerstown, Maryland, and some directly in Chambersburg. Our red morocco volume is one of a dozen examined bindings by the same anonymous binder. This skilled craftsman and sensitive designer worked at least between 1837 and 1843, most likely in Chambersburg itself.

REFERENCE: M. A. Foltz, "A Notable Publication House in Chambersburg—1835–1864," *Papers Read before the Kittochtinny Historical Society* (1908), pp. 183–199.

45a A Boston Binding by Benjamin Bradley, ca. 1845.

John Bartholomew Gough, 1817–1886.
An Autobiography. Fourteenth thousand.
Boston: Published by and for the author, 1845.

16.3 × 10.3 × 1.5 cm.

Brown ribbed cloth; blind-stamped boards and spine fillets; gilt-lettered spine title.

In 1832 Benjamin Bradley established the first American bindery to specialize in cloth work. He pioneered in edition binding, doing not only all the work for such Boston publishers as Ticknor and Fields but also early work for D. Appleton & Company of New York. Bradley frequently offered a variety of bindings for the same book, ranging from simple cloth to elaborately gilt-tooled presentation bindings.

REFERENCE: Frank E. Comparato, *Books for the Millions* (Harrisburg, 1971), pp. 102–103.

45b A Boston Binding by Benjamin Bradley, 1847.

John Bartholomew Gough, 1817–1886.
An Autobiography. Twentieth edition.
Boston: Published by and for the author, 1847.

16.2 × 10.2 × 1.3 cm.

Black ribbed cloth; gilt-stamped boards and spine; glossy yellow endpapers.

Embossed oval blind seal on front fly leaf: "From Bradleys".

PROVENANCE: Inscribed "Mr and Mrs P. Osterhoudt with the Respects of John B. Gough".

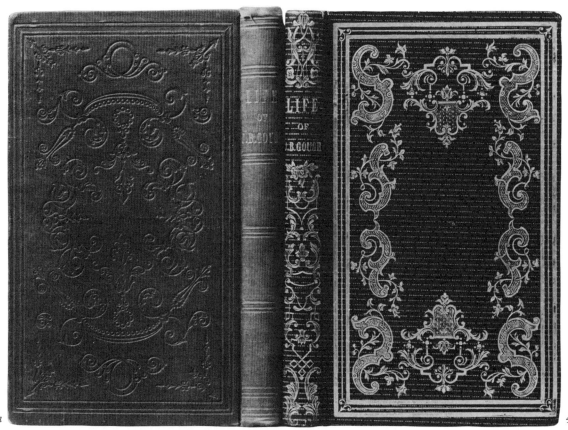

45a

45b

46   A Philadelphia Binding, ca. 1845.

James Hervey, 1713–1758.
Meditations and Contemplations.
Philadelphia: Sorin and Ball, 1845.

19 × 12.2 × 2.9 cm.

Red morocco; blind- and gilt-stamped boards; gilt-lettered and stamped spine; yellow glazed
endpapers; all edges gilt.

In the mid-1840s there was a flowering of composite-plaque bindings on which the design
descends from the top of the board and its mirror image ascends from the bottom. Many of
these bindings, decorating both books and albums, emanated from Philadelphia. Frequently
the central unit of the composition was changed from front to back to add variety. The central
tool on the front board copies an engraving on the half-title. The tool of the country church, on
the rear board, reappears in two known variant bindings on the Philadelphia 1846 edition of
Thomas Gray's *Elegy*, published by John W. Moore.

46

47 An Albany, New York, Binding by Anthony L. Harrison, 1847.

The Rainbow, 1847. Edited by A. J. McDonald.
Albany: A. L. Harrison; New York: Bell and Gould, 1847.

20.6 × 13.4 × 3.4 cm.

Beige calf; gilt-stamped boards and spine, with multicolored onlays; gilt-lettered spine; gold and blue decorated endpapers printed to imitate doublures; all edges gilt.

"A. L. Harrison Binder" stamped in gilt at head of spine; "Patent Stereographic Binding." stamped in gilt at foot of spine.

This binding is unusually successful from a technical point of view. It reflects a style of the time, though the style did not gain wide popularity. Harrison is known to have been active in Albany between 1845 and 1853. Regarding the "Patent Stereographic Binding," a U. S. Patent and Trademark Office search did not reveal a patent issued to Harrison.

REFERENCES: William Loring Andrews, *Bibliopegy in the United States and Kindred Subjects* (New York, 1902), p. 116; Sue Allen, "Machine-Stamped Bookbindings, 1834–1860," *Antiques*, vol. 115 (1979), p. 571.

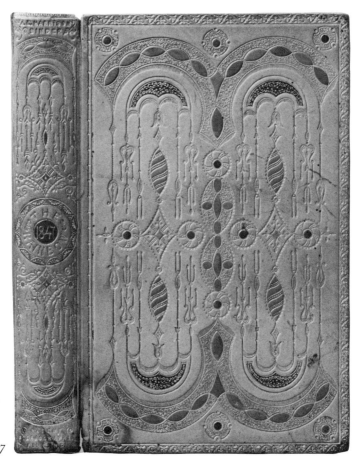

47

48 A Philadelphia Binding by Lippincott & Co., ca. 1848.

William Jerdan, 1782–1869.
The Portrait Annual of Illustrious and Eminent Personages of the Nineteenth Century.
London: Fisher, Son, & Co., 1839.

26.1 × 17.9 × 3.5 cm.

Maroon morocco; gilt- and blind-tooled boards; gilt-lettered and tooled spine; gilt board edges and turn-ins; pink printed endpapers; all edges gilt.

Binder's label inside front cover.

Philadelphia's Joshua Ballinger Lippincott (1814–1886) was typical of America's nineteenth-century entrepreneurs. At fourteen he was hired as a clerk in a bookshop; at eighteen he was appointed manager; and at twenty-two he bought his own business with the money he had saved. He was credited with an intuitive taste for the handsome bindings which made his work so desired by booksellers. In time he was to turn his operation into a major printing, publishing and binding empire. In 1850, at the age of thirty-six, he bought the entire stock of Grigg & Elliott, who had the largest holdings of books and stationery in the country. Within two years his firm had more than five-hundred employees; and the bindery, described at the time in *Godey's Lady's Book*, was a major part of his enterprise.

PROVENANCE: Penciled note, "Light Maroon Super Extra Van Syckle"; inscribed "E. Goddard".

REFERENCES: C. T. Hinckley, "A Day at the Bookbindery of Lippincott, Grambo, & Co.," *Godey's Lady's Book*, vol. 45 (1852), pp. 402–412; J. C. Derby, *Fifty Years Among Authors, Books and Publishers* (New York, 1884), pp. 382–388; J. B. Lippincott Company, *The Author and His Audience* (Philadelphia, 1967), pp. 73–76.

48

49a   A New York Binding for Carlton & Porter, ca. 1849.

Methodist Episcopal Church.
Hymns for the Use of the Methodist Episcopal Church. Revised edition.
New York: Carlton & Porter [1849].

12.5 × 8.4 × 3.1 cm.

Brown morocco; boards and spine stamped in dark brown and raised in imitation of strapwork; gilt-lettered spine; blind-tooled edges; yellow glazed endpapers; all edges gilt.

An interesting example of two leather publisher's bindings prepared for the same text but designed for different tastes.

PROVENANCE: Inscribed "Miss Eliza J. Plaskitt From a Friend".

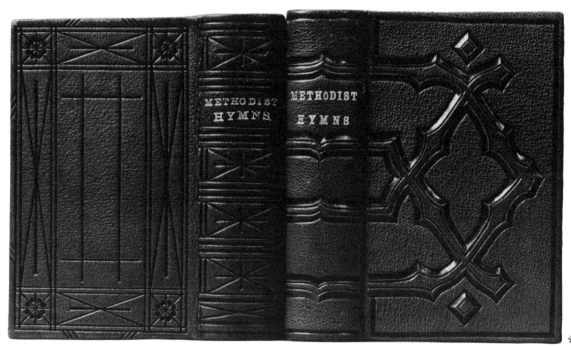

49b   *49a*

49b   A New York Binding for Carlton & Porter, ca. 1849.

Methodist Episcopal Church.
Hymns for the Use of the Methodist Episcopal Church. Revised edition.
New York: Carlton & Porter [1849].

12.2 × 8.5 × 3.4 cm.

Brown morocco; boards and spine stamped in dark brown; gilt-lettered spine; endpapers printed in gold; all edges gilt.

50 A New York Binding for D. Appleton & Company, ca. 1851.

Agnes Strickland, 1796–1874.
The Queens of England.
New York: D. Appleton & Company; Philadelphia: Geo. S. Appleton, 1851.

27 × 18 × 4.2 cm.

Brown morocco on beveled boards, beveling on outside edges; gilt-blocked leather frame, enclosing a reverse-painting-on-glass, attached to blind-tooled front board and matching the gilt-blocked design on back board; gilt-blocked spine; gilt-tooled board edges and turn-ins; all edges gilt.

ILLUSTRATED IN COLOR AS PLATE III FOLLOWING P. 17.

Elaborate publishers' bindings marked the height of Victorian elegance. Experiments in new binding techniques and materials were odd and interesting testimonials to mid-nineteenth century ingenuity. The brightly handcolored illustrations in this volume were reflected in the reverse-painting-on-glass which was inlaid on the front cover. D. Appleton and Company did not begin their own bindery until 1854. The actual designer and producer of this binding is unknown.

51 A New York Binding for Riker, Thorne & Co., ca. 1854.

Frances Sargent Osgood, 1811–1850.
Poems.
New York: Riker, Thorne & Co., copyright 1849 [not published before 1854].

24.5 × 18.5 × 5.6 cm.

Red morocco with white, green and blue leather onlays; gilt-blocked boards with gilt-blocked sunk panels; gilt-blocked spine; gilt-tooled board edges and turn-ins; mock watered-silk endpapers; all edges gilt.

Issued in a velvet-lined hinged leather box.

ILLUSTRATED IN COLOR AS PLATE IV FOLLOWING P. 17.

This extravagantly decorated publishers' binding was produced by the same unidentified firm that produced the simpler trade binding found on most copies of the work. The spine-lettering on both is identical. The central tool of the young lady appears in 1858, well worn, on the back board of the *Atlantic Cable Album*, produced for the New York stationery firm of Eugene Ely.

In his 1856 manual on bookbinding (pp. 227–230), J. B. Nicholson attributes this style to the French and calls it an "Illuminated Binding." He also describes the technique by which such bindings are produced.

REFERENCE: BAL 15352.

52 A Philadelphia Binding by Pawson & Nicholson, ca. 1855.

Augustine Duganne, 1823–1884.
The Poetical Works.
Philadelphia: Parry & McMillan, 1855.

25.4 × 18 × 4.1 cm.

Brown hard-grained morocco on beveled boards; gilt- and blind-tooled boards and spine; gilt-tooled board edges and turn-ins; marbled endpapers; all edges gilt and gauffered.

Stamped on inside of free front endpaper "Bound by Pawson & Nicholson."

ILLUSTRATED IN COLOR AS PLATE V FOLLOWING P. 17.

Philadelphia's foremost binders in the second half of the nineteenth century were Pawson & Nicholson. James Pawson (1802–1891) had come from England and was first listed in the Philadelphia directory for 1839. He was distinguished for his edge gilding, a particularly important aspect of the present binding. James Bartram Nicholson (1820–1901) had worked at various trades before apprenticing to the Philadelphia bookbinders Weaver & Warnick. In 1849, soon after he completed his period of indenture, Nicholson joined Pawson. In 1856 Nicholson published *A Manual of the Art of Bookbinding*, the most substantial work on the subject published in America in the nineteenth century. He retired in 1890 but the firm was continued by his and Pawson's descendants until 1911.

PROVENANCE: Inscribed "E.L.N. from J.B.N.", probably a presentation binding from Nicholson to his mother, Eliza Lowry Nicholson; purchased from Dawson's Book Shop of Los Angeles, 1974, catalog 424, no. 53.
REFERENCES: Papantonio no. 61; *The National Cyclopaedia of American Biography*, vol. 25 (New York, 1936), p. 199.

53a A New York Binding by William Matthews, ca. 1868.

Henry Wadsworth Longfellow, 1807–1882.
The Poetical Works. Revised edition.
Boston: Ticknor and Fields, 1866.

17.9 × 12.4 × 3 cm., 4 volumes.

Brown morocco; boards and spines stamped in dark brown; gilt-lettered spines; gilt-tooled board edges and turn-ins; marbled endpapers; all edges gilt.

"Matthews" stamped on verso of free front endpapers.

William Matthews (1822–1896) was one of several Scottish binders who maintained the standards of excellence in hand binding during the rise of commercial machine binding. Having come to New York in 1843, he started in business for himself in 1846 and won the highest award in competition with foreign binders at the International Exhibition of 1853. Attracting the attention of the publisher David Appleton, he went to work for that firm and soon became head of the bindery, a position he held until his retirement in 1890. In spite of Appleton's huge operation, Matthews never ceased to do fine hand binding.

PROVENANCE: Inscribed "E.G. Lippincott Feb. 14th 1869 from J.W.L."

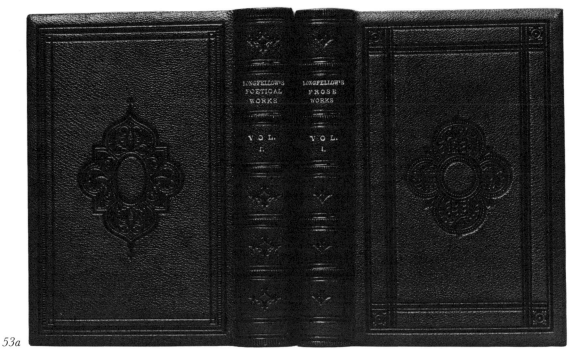

53a   53b

53b   A New York Binding by William Matthews, ca. 1868.

Henry Wadsworth Longfellow, 1807–1882.
The Prose Works. Revised edition.
Boston: Ticknor and Fields, 1866.

17.7 × 12.5 × 3.1 cm., 3 volumes.

Brown morocco; boards and spines stamped in dark brown; gilt-lettered spines; gilt-tooled board edges and turn-ins; marbled endpapers; all edges gilt.

"Matthews" stamped on verso of free front endpapers.

PROVENANCE: Inscribed "EGL Feb. 14. 1869".

54a   A Philadelphia Binding by E. H. Butler & Co., 1868.

William Wordsworth, 1770–1850.
Poems of Nature and Sentiment.
Philadelphia: E. H. Butler & Co., 1868.

20 × 13.0 × 2.1 cm.

Brown morroco; boards and spine stamped in gilt and dark brown; gilt-lettered spine title; dark brown endpapers; all edges gilt.

This pair of publishers' bindings reflects two contrasting fashions of the day. On the one hand were the drab brown bindings, decorated only by a small leaf tool on the spine panels. On the other hand were the elaborate bindings with their multicolored leathers and large gilt plaques. These two volumes incorporate the drab color and simple spines with heavily ornamented boards. One contemporary writer referred to Butler & Company's "inventive genius in the art of ornamentation, capable of bringing forth continually new styles of elegant embellishment."

REFERENCE: Edwin T. Freedley, ed., *United States Mercantile Guide. Leading Pursuits and Leading Men* (Philadelphia, 1856), pp. 86–87.

54a

54b A Philadelphia Binding by E. H. Butler & Co., 1868.

Poetry of the Woods: Passages from the Poets Descriptive of Forest Scenes.
Philadelphia: E. H. Butler & Co., 1868.

20 × 13.8 × 2.1 cm.

Brown morroco; boards and spine stamped in gilt and dark brown; gilt-lettered spine title; dark brown endpapers; all edges gilt.

54b

55 A New York Binding Designed by Helena deKay Gilder, 1876.

Richard Watson Gilder, 1844–1909.
The New Day.
New York: Scribner, Armstrong, 1876.

17.8 × 13.5 × 1.4 cm.

Blue cloth on beveled boards, beveling on outside edges; gilt-stamped front board and gilt-lettered spine; maroon-coated endpapers.

This is R. W. Gilder's first published book. Inspired by Helena deKay, the love sonnets were first published in *Scribner's Monthly* in 1873. In 1874 Gilder married deKay, who then designed the original art work for the book.

REFERENCE: BAL 6536.

55

56 A Boston Binding by Macdonald & Sons, 1885.

Charles H. Brainard, 1817–1885.
John Howard Payne; a Biographical Sketch.
Washington, D.C.: George A. Coolidge, 1885.

25.4 × 18.3 × 2.7 cm.

Brown hard-grained morocco; blind-stamped boards and spine with gilt-tooled author and title; gilt-tooled board edges and turn-ins; simulated watered-silk endpapers; all edges gilt.

Stamped "Bound by Macdonald & Sons" on upper left corner of verso of front flyleaf.

William L. Macdonald, founder of the firm, was joined in the directory listing for 1880 by his sons, Edmund J. and Alexander L. For a decade they worked at 51 Chardon St., operating one of Boston's foremost binderies.

Intaglio dies created their effect by raising the design element and impressing the background, in complete contrast to the way in which gilt and blind stamping were normally done. The design of the boards of this intaglio binding was created with a four part brass die, joined just to the left of the central flower on each of the four sides. By the insertion of extension elements, such dies could be expanded for use on larger volumes.

57 A Boston Binding by Macdonald & Sons, 1887.

Omar Khayyám.
Rubáiyát.
New York: The Grolier Club, 1885.

22.7 × 15.5 × 1.6 cm.

Brown morocco; gilt-tooled boards, spine and board edges; maroon morocco doublures with gilt-tooled dentelles, bordered by gilt-tooled fillets, faced by watered-silk endpapers, backed by marbled fly leaves.

Gilt-stamped "Macdonald & Sons" on lower edge of front doublure.

Macdonald & Sons of Boston created this "Roger Payne" binding for the bibliophile Daniel B. Fearing. Payne (1738–1797) had been the foremost English binder of the eighteenth century. Typical Payne elements include the radiating floral corners and spine panels with their backgrounds formed of dots. Macdonald & Sons, however, achieved their design by the use of corner and spine panel dies which produced in one stroke the effect which Payne had created laboriously, flower by flower and dot by dot, a century earlier. Macdonald & Sons also imitated Payne's brown morocco boards, coupled with maroon doublures.

PROVENANCE: Bookplate of "Daniel B. Fearing, Newport, R.I."

56

57

58   A New York Binding by Stikeman & Co., ca. 1892.

William Loring Andrews, 1837–1920.
Jean Grolier.
New York: The De Vinne Press, 1892.

20.7 × 14.6 × 1.4 cm.

Brown morocco with black morocco inlays in Grolieresque design; gilt-tooled boards; gilt-tooled and lettered spine; gilt board edges; yellow-paper doublures and endpapers, printed in gold and bordered by gilt tooling; top edge gilt.

"Stikeman & Co." stamped in gilt on inside lower front cover.

Between the retirement of William Matthews and the creation of the Club Bindery, New York's two leading binders were James Macdonald and Henry Stikeman. Macdonald's establishment remained a one-on-one hand bindery, whereas Stikeman's was increasingly devoted to the more elegant types of publishers' bindings. In this binding of 1892 one sees the extraordinary skill which Stikeman could achieve in design, inlaying and tooling. With freedom he has created a Grolieresque binding for the Grolier Club's book on Grolier, probably commissioned by Arthur Hawley Scribner.

PROVENANCE: Given to the Bryn Mawr College Library by Helen Annan Scribner, Bryn Mawr Class of 1891.

The front doublure from binding no. 58.

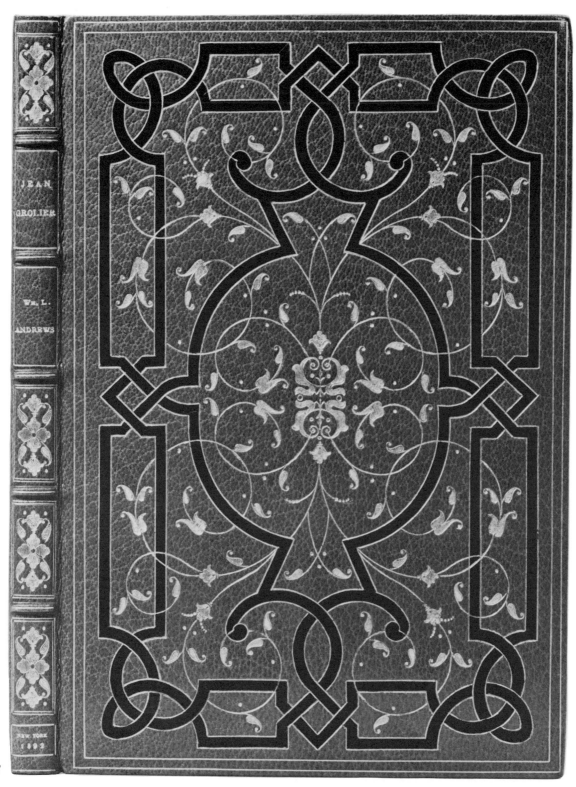

59 A New York Binding Designed by Bertram Grosvenor Goodhue, 1893.

Protestant Episcopal Church.
The Book of Common Prayer.
New York: Printed for the Committee, 1893.

37 × 26.5 × 7 cm.

Vellum on beveled boards, beveling on outside edges; gilt-stamped boards and spine; brass clasps from back cover; gold printed endpapers; top edge gilt.

In 1889 the Convention of the Protestant Episcopal Church appointed a committee to prepare a *Standard Book of Common Prayer,* revising the *Standard* of 1845. This volume, financed by J. Pierpont Morgan, was the result of their efforts. This large-paper edition was printed at the De Vinne Press in New York. "The plan of symbolism and method of decoration were arranged by Mr. Daniel Berkeley Updike: The preparatory studies of plants were made by Mr. William Wells Bosworth: The designs for the borders and cover by Mr. Bertram Grosvenor Goodhue, and the final drawings for reproduction by Mr. Joseph Eliot Hill."

In addition to this copy, the Library owns one of the eleven copies printed on vellum and bound in white (now browned) leather.

PROVENANCE: Signature and bookplate of Francis Goodwin, from the Berkeley Divinity School Library.

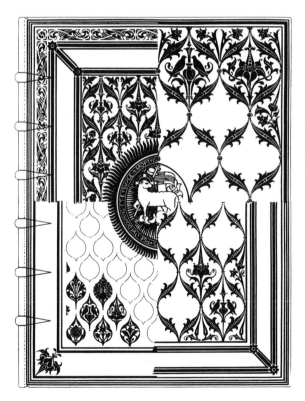

B. G. Goodhue's proposed designs for bindings of D. B. Updike's The Altar Book *(Boston: The Merrymount Press, 1896). Reproduced through the courtesy of the Grolier Club.*

60   A Cornish, New Hampshire, Binding by Frances Arnold, 1903.

Fiona Macleod, pseudonym of William Sharp, 1856–1905.
By Sundown Shores.
Portland, Maine: Thomas B. Mosher, 1902.

12.9 × 8.7 × 1.9 cm.

Light brown morocco; dark brown- and gilt-tooled boards, with gilt-lettering on boards and date on spine; gilt-tooled spine, board edges and turn-ins; all edges gilt.

"FA 1903" stamped in gilt at foot of inside back cover.

Inspired in part by the Arts & Crafts Movement and in part by the Cornish Colony which grew up around the sculptor Augustus Saint-Gaudens, Frances Arnold (1874–1975) was one of a group of American women who early turned their hands to bookbinding. She was a member of Bryn Mawr Class of 1897 and a life-long activist in many fields. Until her death at age 100, Miss Arnold kept "The Bindery" as a warm and interesting corner of her New Hampshire home.

PROVENANCE: Given by bequest to the Bryn Mawr College Library by Frances Arnold.

60

Anna E. Berger at the Club Bindery. Photograph by Mabel Osgood Wright.
(See following entry.)

Anna Berger, who had been trained at the Club Bindery, was responsible for paper restoration. She washed, resized and retinted the leaves. She filled wormholes, mended torn leaves and patched missing pieces with old paper until one could scarcely relocate the original imperfection.

61 A New York Binding by the Club Bindery, 1907.

Camille Lemonnier, 1844–1913.
Les Maris de Mlle Nounouche.
Paris: H. Floury, 1906.

23.8 × 18.9 × 3.1 cm.

Citron morocco with multicolored inlays in a mosaic design; gilt-tooled boards; gilt-tooled and lettered spine, gilt board edges; citron morocco doublures with gilt-tooled beaded border and monogram of Robert Hoe, bordered by gilt-tooled fillets, faced by silk endpapers, backed by marbled fly leaves; all edges gilt.

"The Club Bindery 1907, Leon Maillard Finisher" stamped in gilt on lower edge of front doublure.

In 1884 New York's leading bibliophiles created the Grolier Club, an organization designed to further the interests of America's enthusiastic new book collectors. These men were acquiring their treasures more rapidly than America's few hand binders could handle them. Reluctant to ship them back to Europe for repairs or rebinding, they determined to establish their own bindery. They turned to fellow Club member and bookbinder William Matthews (no. 53) for guidance. Binders and tools alike were sought both here and abroad. Several of Europe's great binders were brought to New York, and by 1895 the Club Bindery was a reality. Until its final days, in 1909, the bindery produced the finest bindings in America. Details of its history are interestingly chronicled in Elbert and Lawrence Thompson's study.

PROVENANCE: Booklabel "Ex Libris Robert Hoe"; given to the Bryn Mawr College Library by Alba Boardman Johnson, Bryn Mawr Class of 1889.

REFERENCE: Elbert A. Thompson and Lawrence S. Thompson, *Fine Binding in America* (Urbana, 1956).

Leon Maillard at the Club Bindery.
Photograph by Mabel Osgood Wright.

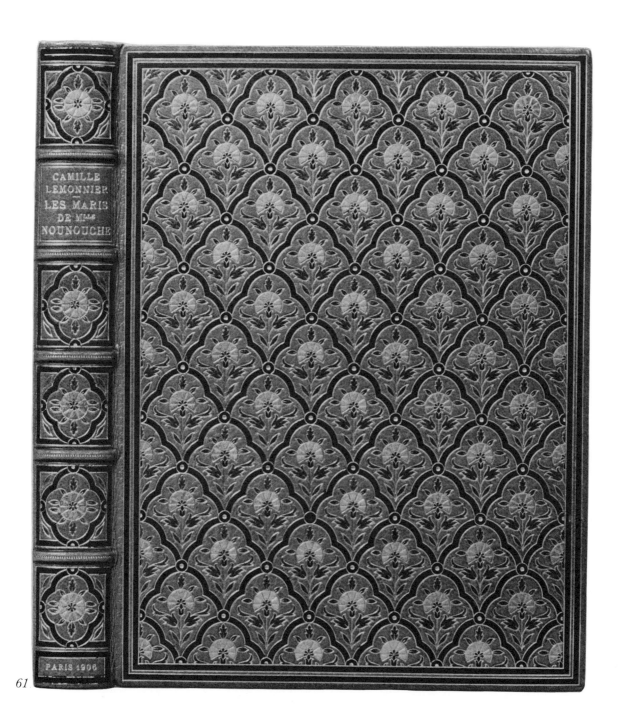

61

62 A New York Binding by James Macdonald, 1909.

[*Souvenir volume for*] *a little dinner given to Mr. Charles Scribner and Mr. Arthur Hawley Scribner.*
[New York, 1909.]

25 × 18.9 × 1.8 cm.

Blue morocco; gilt- and blind-tooled boards, gilt-tooled spine and board edges; marbled-paper doublures bordered by gilt tooling; top edge gilt; "Arthur Hawley Scribner" stamped in gilt on front cover.

"Macdonald—N.Y." stamped in gilt on lower turn-in on back board.

In 1873 James Macdonald (1850–1920) left Glasgow for New York. Trained in bookbinding, he attached himself to New York's master binder, another Scot, William Matthews (no. 53). By 1880 he had saved enough to start the bookbinding firm which continues as James Macdonald Company to this day. The dies and tools used for the boards of this binding are still in the possession of the company. The four corner units are separate pieces. By double stamping, the gilt and blind decorations resulted from the same die. The corners were then connected by the use of fillet rolls. After the demise of the Club Bindery (no. 61), Macdonald acquired many of their tools, some of which are still in use by the firm.

PROVENANCE: Bound for Arthur Hawley Scribner; presented to the Bryn Mawr College Library by Mr Scribner's wife, Helen Annan Scribner, Bryn Mawr Class of 1891.

REFERENCE: "The Editors' Attic," *Antiques,* vol. 53 (1948), p. 222.

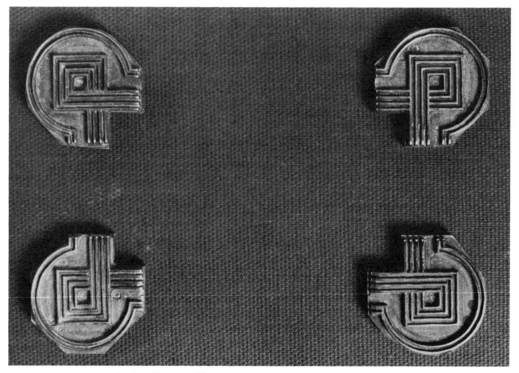

The dies used in creating binding no. 62.

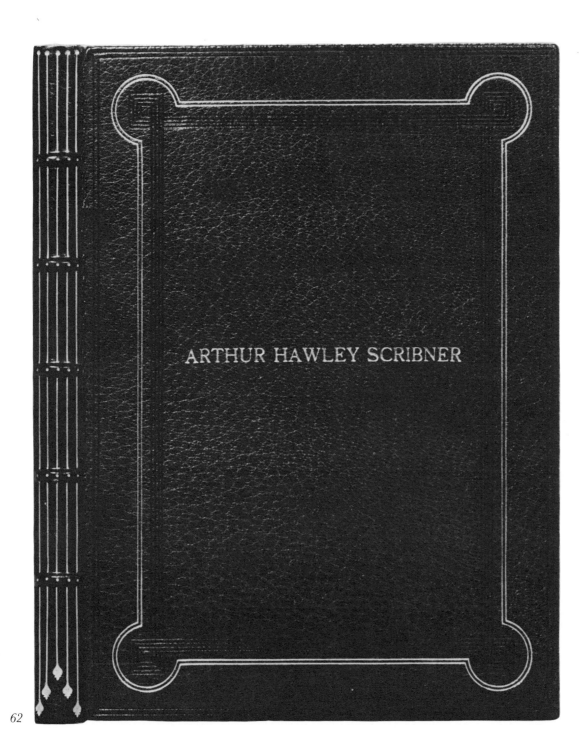

Bibliography

Books Referred to by Abbreviated Citations

BAL   Blanck, Jacob Nathaniel. *Bibliography of American Literature.* New York, 1955-

Evans   Evans, Charles. *American Bibliography: A Chronological Dictionary of all Books, Pamphlets, and Periodical Publications Printed in the United States of America,* 1903; rpt. New York, 1941-1942.

Papantonio   *Early American Bookbindings from the Collection of Michael Papantonio.* New York, 1972.

Shaw & Shoemaker Shaw, Ralph Robert, and Richard H. Shoemaker. *American Bibliography: A Preliminary Checklist for 1801-1819.* New York, 1958-1966.

Shoemaker   Shoemaker, Richard H. *A Checklist of American Imprints for 1820-1829.* New York, 1964-1971.

Wing   Wing, Donald Goddard. *Short-title Catalogue of Books Printed in England, Scotland, Ireland, Wales, and British America, and of English Books Printed in other Countries, 1641-1700.* New York, 1945-1951.

Selected General Studies

Allen, Sue. "Machine-Stamped Bookbindings, 1834-1860." *Antiques,* vol. 115 (1979), pp. 564-572.

Andrews, William Loring. *Bibliopegy in the United States and Kindred Subjects.* New York, 1902.

Bookbinding in America. Ed. Hellmut Lehmann-Haupt. New York, 1967; includes "Early American Bookbinding by Hand, 1636-1820" by Hannah D. French; "The Rise of American Edition Binding" by Joseph W. Rogers; and "On the Rebinding of Old Books" by Hellmut Lehmann-Haupt. Addendum found in Albert Ehrman, "Early American Bookbinders," The Bibliographical Society of America, *Papers,* vol. 35 (1941), pp. 210-211.

Comparato, Frank E. *Books for the Millions.* Harrisburg, 1971.

Ellenport, Samuel B. *An Essay on the Development & Usage of Brass Plate Dies, Including a Catalogue Raisonné from the Collection of The Harcourt Bindery.* Boston, 1980.

Foot, Mirjam M. *The Henry Davis Gift: A Collection of Bookbindings.* Vols. 1 & 2. London, 1978-1983.

Matthews, William. *Modern Bookbinding Practically Considered.* New York, 1889.

McLean, Ruari. *Victorian Book Design and Colour Printing.* Berkeley, 1972.

McLean, Ruari. *Victorian Publishers' Book-Bindings in Cloth and Leather.* Berkeley, 1973.

McLean, Ruari. *Victorian Publishers' Book-Bindings in Paper.* London, 1983.

Nicholson, James B. *A Manual of the Art of Bookbinding.* Philadelphia, 1856.

Roberts, Matt T., and Don Etherington. *Bookbinding and the Conservation of Books; a Dictionary of Descriptive Terminology.* Washington, D.C., 1982.

Walters Art Gallery. *The History of Bookbinding, 525-1950 A.D.* Baltimore, 1957.

Indexes

Indexes

Numbers refer to the entries

INDEX OF BINDERS

(including Binders' Shops, Designers, etc.)

INDEX OF PLACES

(Places indicate where the books were bound)
Year in parenthesis refers to the year of binding

New York (*continued*)
   (1868) 53b, (1876) 55, (1892) 58, (1893) 59,
   (1907) 61, (1909) 62
Philadelphia   (1730) 5, (1763) 11, (1793) 18a,
   (1793) 18b, (1799) 17, (1812) 27, (1823) 35a,
   (1823) 35b, (1829) 40a, (1829) 40b, (1837)
43a, (1839) 43b, (1845) 46, (1848) 48,
   (1855) 52, (1868) 54a, (1868) 54b
Philadelphia County   (1762) 16b, (1784) 15,
   (1791) 16a
Reading, Pennsylvania   (1824) 36

INDEX OF PROVENANCE

Adams, E.   39
Adrianz   3
Archer, Benjamin   35a, 35b
Arnold, Frances   60
Baer, Jacob   31
Bauman, Christian   11
Baumanni, Frau Ja   11
Baumanni, Marry   11
Bear, John   11
Berkeley Divinity School   59
Bingham, John Junr   13
Bingham, John Senr   13
Bodine, John   3
Boston Athn   1
Brewer, Deacon   4
Brown, Louisa M.   42
C., T.   9
Carvill, M.   29
Chandler, John   4
Chandler, Samuel   4
Clay, Miss Catharine   33a
DaCosta, Dr J. Chalmers   27
DaCosta, George T.   27
Dearden, Robert R.   4
Dunlap, John   12
Elton   42
Elvin, Richard   2
Evans, Owen   5
Farrar, Ephm H.   21
Fearing, Daniel B.   57
Felt, Joseph B.   1
Fleet, Thomas   6
Foering, Margaret   40a
Freedman, Max   24a, 24b
Goddard, E.   48
Goodwin, Francis   59
Gough, John B.   45b

Griscom, Genevieve Ludlow   25
Harvey, Isaac Jr   17
Hillyer, John   3
Hoe, Robert   61
Hoitt, Ira B.   22
Hulme, Thomas   29
Hurst   26
Ingram, Jno.   12
Jackson, Mrs W. H.   43a
Janvier, George W.   18b
Janvier, Mary   18b
Johnson, Alba Boardman   61
Johnston, N.   22
Jotter, Johannes   32
Kane, John   19
Kent, Mary M.   34
Krick, Isaac   36
L, EG   53b
L., I. W.   33a
L., J. W.   53a
Leary   17
Lippincott, E. G.   53a
Lowder, Ann   10
Maine Charity School   1
Mather, Increase   1
Mather, Richard   1
N., E. L.   52
N., J. B.   52
Nicholson, Eliza Lowry   52
Orne, C. H.   28
Osterhoudt, Mr and Mrs P.   45b
Parmly, Mrs   39
Pegner, Jacob   11
Perkins, Anna D.   30
Plaskitt, Catharine Ann   41
Plaskitt, Miss Eliza J.   49a
Redfield, W. C.   37

INDEX OF AUTHORS & TITLES

Bookbinding in America: 1680–1910

DESIGNED BY DOUGLASS S. LIVINGSTON AND
KIM GARRETT OF SUTTER HOUSE, LITITZ,
PENNSYLVANIA. COMPOSED IN BASKERVILLE
WITH DISPLAY LINES IN AMERICANA BY
ARROWSMITH TYPOGRAPHERS, ALSO OF LITITZ.
TEXT AND COLORPLATES PRINTED BY
SCIENCE PRESS, EPHRATA, PENNSYLVANIA,
ON MOHAWK SUPERFINE SMOOTH SOFTWHITE
AND WARREN LUSTRO OFFSET ENAMEL
CREAM DULL. BOUND BY MURPHY-PARKER
OF PHILADELPHIA IN SCHOLCO ALMOLINE
CLOTH BY VAN HEEK TEXTILES, THE
NETHERLANDS, DISTRIBUTED BY HARCOURT
BINDERY OF BOSTON.